The Theory and Practice
of Model Aeroplaning

V. E. Johnson

Alpha Editions

This edition published in 2023

ISBN : 9789357941273

Design and Setting By
Alpha Editions
www.alphaedis.com
Email - info@alphaedis.com

Contents

PREFACE

The object of this little book is not to describe how to construct some particular kind of aeroplane; this has been done elsewhere: but to narrate in plain language the general practice and principles of model aeroplaning.

There is a *science* of model aeroplaning—just as there is a science of model yachting and model steam and electric traction, and an endeavour is made in the following pages to do in some measure for model aeroplanes what has already been done for model yachts and locomotives. To achieve the best results, theory and practice must go hand in hand.

From a series of carefully conducted experiments empirical formulæ can be obtained which, combined later with mathematical induction and deduction, may lead, not only to a more accurate and generalized law than that contained in the empirical formula, but to valuable deductions of a totally new type, embodying some general law hitherto quite unknown by experimentalists, which in its turn may serve as a foundation or stepping stone for suggesting other experiments and empirical formulæ which may be of especial importance, to be treated in *their* turn like their predecessor. By "especial importance," I mean not only to "model," but "Aeroplaning" generally.

As to the value of experiments on or with models with respect to full-sized machines, fifteen years ago I held the opinion that they were a very doubtful factor. I have since considerably modified that view, and now consider that experiments with models—if properly carried out, and given[vi] due, not *undue*, weight—both can and will be of as much use to the science of Aeronautics as they have already proved themselves to be in that of marine engineering.

The subject of model propellers and motors has been somewhat fully dealt with, as but little has been published (in book form, at any rate) on these all-important departments. On similar grounds the reasons why and how a model aeroplane flies have been practically omitted, because these have been dealt with more or less in every book on heavier-than-air machines.

Great care has been exercised in the selection of matter, and in the various facts stated herein; in most cases I have personally verified them; great pains have also been exercised to exclude not only misleading, but also doubtful matter. I have no personal axe to grind whatever, nor am I connected either directly or indirectly with any firm of aeroplane builders, model or otherwise.

The statements contained in these pages are absolutely free from bias of any kind, and for them I am prepared to accept full responsibility.

I have to thank Messrs. A.W. GAMAGE (Holborn) for the use of various model parts for testing purposes, and also for the use of various electros from their modern Aviation Catalogue; also Messrs. T.W.K. CLARKE & CO., of Kingston-on-Thames. For the further use of electros, and for permission to reproduce illustrations which have previously appeared in their papers, I must express my acknowledgment and thanks to the publishers of the "Model Engineer," "Flight," and the "Aero." Corrections and suggestions of any kind will be gratefully received, and duly acknowledged.

V.E. JOHNSON.

GLOSSARY OF TERMS USED IN MODEL AEROPLANING.

Aeroplane. A motor-driven flying machine which relies upon surfaces for its support in the air.

Monoplane (single). An aeroplane with one pair of outstretched wings.

Aerofoil. These outstretched wings are often called aerofoil surfaces. One pair of wings forming one aerofoil surface.

Monoplane (double). An aeroplane with two aerofoils, one behind the other or two main planes, tandem-wise.

Biplane. An aeroplane with two aerofoils, one below the other, or having two main planes superposed.

Triplane. An aeroplane having three such aerofoils or three such main planes.

Multiplane. Any such machine having more than three of the above.

Glider. A motorless aeroplane.

Helicopter. A flying machine in which propellers are employed to raise the machine in the air by their own unaided efforts.

Dihedral Angle. A dihedral angle is an angle made by two surfaces that do not lie in the same plane, i.e. when the aerofoils are arranged V-shaped. It is better, however, to somewhat extend this definition, and not to consider it as necessary that the two surfaces *do* actually meet, but would do so if produced thus in figure. BA and CD are still dihedrals, sometimes termed "upturned tips."

Dihedrals.

Span is the distance from tip to tip of the main supporting surface measured transversely (across) the line of flight.

Camber (a slight arching or convexity upwards). This term denotes that the aerofoil has such a curved transverse section.

Chord is the distance between the entering (or leading) edge of the main supporting surface (aerofoil) and the trailing edge of the same; also defined as the fore and aft dimension of the main planes measured in a straight line between the leading and trailing edges.

Aspect Ratio is $^{span}/_{chord}$

Gap is the vertical distance between one aerofoil and the one which is immediately above it.

(The gap is usually made equal to the chord).

Angle of Incidence. The angle of incidence is the angle made by the chord with the line of flight.

AB = chord.   AB = cambered surface.

SP = line of flight. ASP = α = L of incidence.

Width. The width of an aerofoil is the distance from the front to the rear edge, allowing for camber.

Length. This term is usually applied to the machine as a whole, from the front leading edge of elevator (or supports) to tip of tail.

Arched. This term is usually applied to aerofoil surfaces which dip downwards like the wings of a bird. The curve in this case being at right angles to "camber." A surface can, of course, be both cambered and arched.

Propeller. A device for propelling or pushing an aeroplane forward or for raising it vertically (lifting screw).

Tractor Screw. A device for pulling the machine (used when the propeller is placed in the front of the machine).

Keel. A vertical plane or planes (usually termed "fins") arranged longitudinally for the purposes of stability and steering.

Tail. The plane, or group of planes, at the rear end of an aeroplane for the purpose chiefly of giving longitudinal stability. In such cases the tail is normally (approx.) horizontal, but not unfrequently vertical tail-pieces are fitted as well for steering (transversely) to the right or left, or the entire tail may be twisted for the purpose of transverse stability (vide *Elevator*). Such[xv] appendages are being used less and less with the idea of giving actual support.

Rudder is the term used for the vertical plane, or planes, which are used to steer the aeroplane sideways.

Warping. The flexing or bending of an aerofoil out of its normal shape. The rear edges near the tips of the aerofoil being dipped or tilted respectively, in order to create a temporary difference in their inclinations to the line of flight. Performed in conjunction with rudder movements, to counteract the excessive action of the latter.

Ailerons (also called "righting-tips," "balancing-planes," etc.). Small aeroplanes in the vicinity of the tips of the main aerofoil for the purpose of assisting in the maintenance of equilibrium or for steering purposes either with or without the assistance of the rudder.

Elevator. The plane, or planes, in front of the main aerofoil used for the purpose of keeping the aeroplane on an even keel, or which cause (by being tilted or dipped) the aeroplane to rise or fall (vide *Tail*).

INTRODUCTION.

§ 1. Model Aeroplanes are primarily divided into two classes: first, models intended before all else to be ones that shall *fly*; secondly, *models*, using the word in its proper sense of full-sized machines. Herein model aeroplanes differ from model yachts and model locomotives. An extremely small model locomotive *built to scale* will still *work*, just as a very small yacht built to scale will *sail*; but when you try to build a scale model of an "Antoinette" monoplane, *including engine*, it cannot be made to fly unless the scale be a very large one. If, for instance, you endeavoured to make a 1/10 scale model, your model petrol motor would be compelled to have eight cylinders, each 0·52 bore, and your magneto of such size as easily to pass through a ring half an inch in diameter. Such a model could not possibly work.[1]

> *Note.*—Readers will find in the "Model Engineer" of June 16, 1910, some really very fine working drawings of a prize-winning Antoinette monoplane model.

§ 2. Again, although the motor constitutes the *chief*, it is by no means the sole difficulty in *scale* model aeroplane building. To reproduce to scale at *scale weight*, or indeed anything approaching it, *all* the *necessary*—in the case of a full-sized machine—framework is not possible in a less than 1/5 scale.

§ 3. Special difficulties occur in the case of any prototype taken. For instance, in the case of model Blériots it is extremely difficult to get the centre of gravity sufficiently forward.

§ 4. Scale models of actual flying machines *that will fly* mean models *at least* 10 or 12 feet across, and every other dimension in like proportion; and it must always be carefully borne in mind that the smaller the scale the greater the difficulties, but not in the same proportion—it would not be *twice* as difficult to build a ¼-in. scale model as a ½-in., but *four, five* or *six* times as difficult.

§ 5. Now, the *first* requirement of a model aeroplane, or flying machine, is that it shall FLY.

As will be seen later on—unless the machine be of large size, 10 feet and more spread—the only motor at our disposal is the motor of twisted rubber strands, and this to be efficient requires to be long, and is of practically uniform weight throughout; this alone alters the entire *distribution of weight* on the machine and makes:

§ 6. "**Model Aeroplaning an Art in itself**," and as such we propose to consider it in the following pages.

We have said that the first requisite of a model aeroplane is that it shall fly, but there is no necessity, nor is it indeed always to be desired, that this should be its only one, unless it be built with the express purpose of obtaining a record length of flight. For ordinary flights and scientific study what is required is a machine in which minute detail is of secondary importance, but which does along its main lines "*approximate* to the real thing."

§ 7. Simplicity should be the first thing aimed at—simplicity means efficiency, it means it in full-sized machines, still more does it mean it in models—and this very question of simplicity brings us to that most important question of all, namely, the question of *weight*.

CHAPTER I.
THE QUESTION OF WEIGHT.

§ 1. The following is an extract from a letter that appeared in the correspondence columns of "The Aero."[2]

> "To give you some idea how slight a thing will make a model behave badly, I fitted a skid to protect the propeller underneath the aeroplane, and the result in retarding flight could be seen very quickly, although the weight of the skid was almost nil.[3] To all model makers who wish to make a success I would say, strip all that useless and heavy chassis off, cut down the 'good, honest stick' that you have for a backbone to half its thickness, stay it with wire if it bends under the strain of the rubber, put light silk on the planes, and use an aluminium[4] propeller. The result will surpass all expectations."

§ 2. The above refers, of course, to a rubber-motor driven model. Let us turn to a steam-driven prototype. I take the best known example of all, Professor Langley's famous model. Here is what the professor has to say on the question[5]:—

> "Every bit of the machinery had to be constructed with scientific accuracy. It had to be tested again and again. The difficulty of getting the machine light enough was such that every part of it had to be remade several times. It would be in full working order when something would give way, and this part would have to be strengthened. This caused additional weight, and necessitated cutting off so much weight from some other part of the machinery. At times the difficulty seemed almost heartbreaking; but I went on, piece by piece and atom by atom, until I at last succeeded in getting all the parts of the right strength and proportion."

How to obtain the maximum strength with the minimum of weight is one of the, if not the most, difficult problems which the student has to solve.

§ 3. The theoretical reason why *weight* is such an all-important item in model aeroplaning, much more so than in the case of full-size machines, is that, generally speaking, such models do not fly fast enough to possess a high weight carrying capacity. If you increase the area of the supporting surface you increase also the resistance, and thereby diminish the speed, and are no better off than before. The only way to increase the weight carrying capacity of a model is to increase its speed. This point will be recurred to later on.

One of Mr. T.W.K. Clarke's well-known models, surface area 1¼ sq. ft., weight 1¼ lb., is stated to have made a flight of 300 yards carrying 6 oz. of lead. This works out approximately at 21 oz. per sq. ft.

The velocity (speed) is not stated, but some earlier models by the same designer, weight 1½ lb., supporting area 1½ sq. ft., i.e., at rate of 16 oz. per sq. ft., travelled at a rate of 37 ft. per second, or 25 miles an hour.

The velocity of the former, therefore, would certainly not be less than 30 miles an hour.

§ 4. Generally speaking, however, models do not travel at anything like this velocity, or carry anything like this weight per sq. ft.

An average assumption of 13 to 15 miles an hour does nor err on the minimum side. Some very light fabric covered models have a speed of less than even 10 miles an hour. Such, of course, cannot be termed efficient models, and carry only about 3 oz. per sq. ft. Between these two types—these two extremes—somewhere lies the "Ideal Model."

The maximum of strength with the minimum of weight can be obtained only:—

1. By a knowledge of materials.

2. Of how to combine those materials in a most efficient and skilful manner.

3. By a constant use of the balance or a pair of scales, and noting (in writing) the weight and result of every trial and every experiment in the alteration and change of material used. WEIGH EVERYTHING.

§ 5. The reader must not be misled by what has been said, and think that a model must not weigh anything if it is to fly well. A heavy model will fly much better against the wind than a light one, provided that the former *will* fly. To do this it must fly *fast*. To do this again it must be well powered, and offer the minimum of resistance to the medium through which it moves. This means its aerofoil (supporting) surfaces must be of polished wood or metal. This point brings us to the question of Resistance, which we will now consider.

CHAPTER II.
THE QUESTION OF RESISTANCE.

§ 1. It is, or should be, the function of an aeroplane—model or otherwise—to pass through the medium in which it travels in such a manner as to leave that medium in as motionless a state as possible, since all motion of the surrounding air represents so much power wasted.

Every part of the machine should be so constructed as to move through the air with the minimum of disturbance and resistance.

§ 2. The resistance, considered as a percentage of the load itself, that has to be overcome in moving a load from one place to another, is, according to Mr. F.W. Lanchester, 12½ per cent. in the case of a flying machine, and 0·1 per cent. in the case of a cargo boat, and of a solid tyre motor car 3 per cent., a locomotive 1 per cent. Four times at least the resistance in the case of aerial locomotion has to be overcome to that obtained from ordinary locomotion on land. The above refer, of course, to full-sized machines; for a model the resistance is probably nearer 14 or 15 per cent.

§ 3. This resistance is made up of—

- 1. Aerodynamic resistance.
- 2. Head resistance.
- 3. Skin-friction (surface resistance).

The first results from the necessity of air supporting the model during flight.

The second is the resistance offered by the framework, wires, edges of aerofoils, etc.

The third, skin-friction or surface resistance, is very small at low velocities, but increases as the square of the velocity. To reduce the resistance which it sets up, all surfaces used should be as smooth as possible. To reduce the second, contours of ichthyoid, or fish-like, form should be used, so that the resultant stream-line flow of the medium shall keep in touch with the surface of the body.

§ 4. As long ago as 1894 a series of experiments were made by the writer[6] to solve the following problem: given a certain length and breadth, to find the shape which will offer the least resistance. The experiments were made with a whirling table 40 ft. in diameter, which could be rotated so that the extremity of the arm rotated up to a speed of 45 miles an hour. The method of experimenting was as follows: The bodies (diam. 4 in.) were balanced against one another at the extremity of the arm, being so balanced that their motions forward and backward were parallel. Provision was made for accurately balancing the parallel scales on which the bodies were suspended without altering the resistance offered by the apparatus to the air. Two experiments at least (to avoid error) were made in each case, the bodies being reversed in the second experiment, the top one being put at the bottom, and *vice versa*. The conclusions arrived at were:—

For minimum (head) resistance a body should have—

1. Its greatest diameter two-fifths of its entire length from its head.

2. Its breadth and its depth in the proportion of four to three.

3. Its length at least from five to nine times its greatest breadth (nine being better than five).

4. A very tapering form of stern, the actual stern only being of just sufficient size to allow of the propeller shaft passing through. In the case of twin propellers some slight modification of the stern would be necessary.

5. Every portion of the body in contact with the fluid to be made as smooth as possible.

6. A body of such shape gives at most only *one-twentieth* the resistance offered by a flat disk of similar maximum sectional area.

Results since fully confirmed.

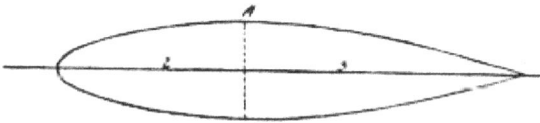

Fig. 1.—Shape of Least Resistance.

The design in Fig. 2 is interesting, not only because of its probable origin, but because of the shape of the body and arrangement of the propellers; no rudder is shown, and the long steel vertical mast extending both upwards and downwards through the centre would render it suitable only for landing on water.

§ 5. In the case of a rubber-driven model, there is no containing body part, so to speak, a long thin stick, or tubular construction if preferred, being all that is necessary.

The long skein of elastic, vibrating as well as untwisting as it travels with the machine through the air, offers some appreciable resistance, and several experimenters have *enclosed* it in a light tube made of *very thin* veneer wood rolled and glued, or paper even may be used; such tubes can be made very light, and possess considerable rigidity, especially longitudinally. If the model be a biplane, then all the upright struts between the two aerofoils should be given a shape, a vertical section of which is shown in Fig. 3.

§ 6. In considering this question of resistance, the substance of which the aerofoil surface is made plays a very important part, as well as whether that surface be plane or curved. For some reason not altogether easy to determine, fabric-covered planes offer *considerably* more resistance than wooden or metal ones. That they should offer *more* resistance is what common sense would lead one to expect, but hardly to the extent met with in actual practice.

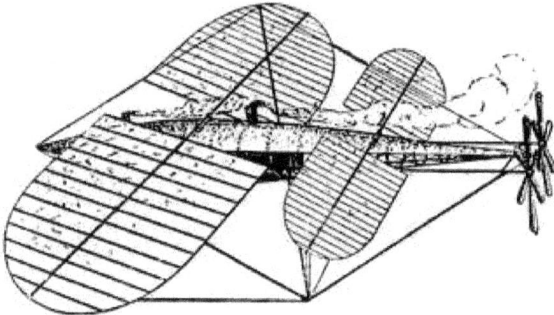

FIG. 2.—DESIGN FOR AN AEROPLANE MODEL (POWER DRIVEN).
THIS DESIGN IS ATTRIBUTED TO PROFESSOR LANGLEY.

Built up fabric-covered aeroplanes[7] *gain in lightness, but lose in resistance.* In the case of curved surfaces this difference is considerably more; one reason, undoubtedly, is that in a built up model surface there is nearly always a tendency to make this curvature excessive, and much more than it should be. Having called attention to this under the head of resistance, we will leave it now to recur to it later when considering the aerofoil proper.

FIG. 3.—HORIZONTAL SECTION OF VERTICAL STRUT (ENLARGED.)

§ 7. Allusion has been made in this chapter to skin friction, but no value given for its coefficient.[8] Lanchester's value for planes from ½ to 1½ sq. ft. in area, moving about 20 to 30 ft. per second, is

$$0 \cdot 009 \text{ to } 0 \cdot 015.$$

Professor Zahm (Washington) gives $0 \cdot 0026$ lb. per sq. ft. at 25 ft. per second, and at 37 ft. per second, $0 \cdot 005$, and the formula

$$f = 0 \cdot 00000778 l^{\cdot 93} v^{1 \cdot 85}$$

f being the average friction in lb. per sq. in., l the length in feet, and v the velocity in ft. per second. He also experimented with various kinds of surfaces, some rough, some smooth, etc.

His conclusion is:—"All even surfaces have approximately the same coefficient of skin friction. Uneven surfaces have a greater coefficient." All formulæ on skin friction must at present be accepted with reserve.

§ 8. The following three experiments, however, clearly prove its *existence*, and *that it has considerable effect*:—

1. A light, hollow celluloid ball, supported on a stream of air projected upwards from a jet, rotates in one direction or the other as the jet is inclined to the left or to the right. (F.W. Lanchester.)

2. When a golf ball (which is rough) is hit so as to have considerable underspin, its range is increased from 135 to 180 yards, due entirely to the greater frictional resistance to the air on that side on which the whirl and the progressive motion combine. (Prof. Tait.)

3. By means of a (weak) bow a golf ball can be made to move point blank to a mark 30 yards off, provided the string be so adjusted as to give a good underspin; adjust the string to the centre of the ball, instead of catching it below, and the drop will be about 8 ft. (Prof. Tait.)

CHAPTER III.
THE QUESTION OF BALANCE.

§ 1. It is perfectly obvious for successful flight that any model flying machine (in the absence of a pilot) must possess a high degree of automatic stability. The model must be so constructed as to be naturally stable, *in the medium through which it is proposed to drive it.* The last remark is of the greatest importance, as we shall see.

§ 2. In connexion with this same question of automatic stability, the question must be considered from the theoretical as well as from the practical side, and the labours and researches of such men as Professors Brian and Chatley, F.W. Lanchester, Captain Ferber, Mouillard and others must receive due weight. Their work cannot yet be fully assessed, but already results have been arrived at far more important than are generally supposed.

The following are a few of the results arrived at from theoretical considerations; they cannot be too widely known.

(A) Surfaces concave on the under side are not stable unless some form of balancing device (such as a tail, etc.) is used.

(B) If an aeroplane is in equilibrium and moving uniformly, it is necessary for stability that it shall tend towards a condition of equilibrium.

(C) In the case of "oscillations" it is absolutely necessary for stability that these oscillations shall decrease in amplitude, in other words, be damped out.

(D) In aeroplanes in which the dihedral angle is excessive or the centre of gravity very low down, a dangerous pitching motion is quite likely to be set up. [Analogy in shipbuilding—an increase in the metacentre height while increasing the stability in a statical sense causes the ship to do the same.]

(E) The propeller shaft should pass through the centre of gravity of the machine.

(F) The front planes should be at a greater angle of inclination than the rear ones.

(G) The longitudinal stability of an aeroplane grows much less when the aeroplane commences to rise, a monoplane becoming unstable when the angle of ascent is greater than the inclination of the main aerofoil to the horizon.

(H) Head resistance increases stability.

(I) Three planes are more stable than two. [Elevator—main aerofoil—horizontal rudder behind.]

(J) When an aeroplane is gliding (downwards) stability is greater than in horizontal flight.

(K) A large moment of inertia is inimical (opposed) to stability.

(M) Aeroplanes (naturally) stable up to a certain velocity (speed) may become unstable when moving beyond that speed. [Possible explanation. The motion of the air over the edges of the aerofoil becomes turbulent, and the form of the stream lines suddenly changes. Aeroplane also probably becomes deformed.]

(N) In a balanced glider for stability a separate surface at a negative angle to the line of flight is essential. [Compare F.]

(O) A keel surface should be situated well above and behind the centre of gravity.

(P) An aeroplane is a conservative system, and stability is greatest when the kinetic energy is a maximum. (Illustration, the pendulum.)

§ 3. Referring to A. Models with a plane or flat surface are not unstable, and will fly well without a tail; such a machine is called a simple monoplane.

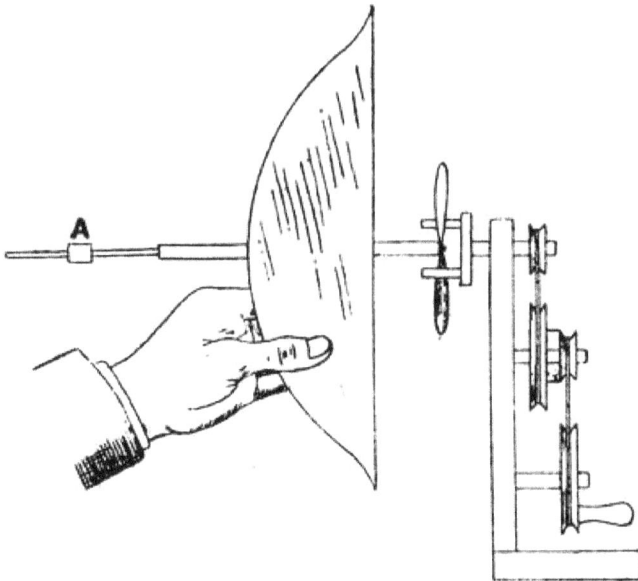

FIG. 4.—ONE OF MR. BURGE WEBB'S SIMPLE MONOPLANES. SHOWING BALANCE WEIGHT A (MOVABLE), AND ALSO HIS WINDING-UP GEAR—A VERY HANDY DEVICE.

§ 4. Referring to D. Many model builders make this mistake, i.e., the mistake of getting as low a centre of gravity as possible under the quite erroneous idea that they are thereby increasing the stability of the machine. Theoretically the *centre of gravity should be the centre of head resistance, as also the centre of pressure.*

In practice some prefer to put the centre of gravity in models *slightly* above the centre of head resistance, the reason being that, generally speaking, wind gusts have a "lifting" action on the machine. It must be carefully borne in mind, however, that if the centre of wind pressure on the aerofoil surface and the centre of gravity do not coincide, no matter at what point propulsive action be applied, it can be proved by quite elementary mechanics that such an arrangement, known as "acentric," produces a couple tending to upset the machine.

This action is the probable cause of many failures.

FIG. 5.—THE STRINGFELLOW MODEL MONOPLANE OF 1848.

§ 5. Referring to E. If the propulsive action does not pass through the centre of gravity the system again becomes "acentric." Even supposing condition D fulfilled, and we arrive at the following most important result, viz., that for stability:—

THE CENTRES OF GRAVITY, OF PRESSURE, OF HEAD RESISTANCE, SHOULD BE COINCIDENT, AND THE PROPULSIVE ACTION OF THE PROPELLER PASS THROUGH THIS SAME POINT.

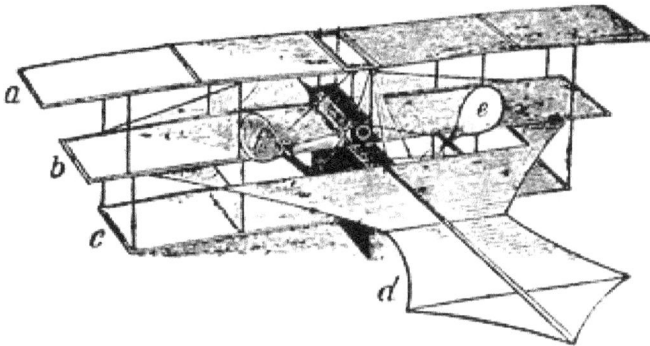

FIG. 6.—THE STRINGFELLOW MODEL TRIPLANE OF 1868.

§ 6. Referring to F and N—the problem of longitudinal stability. There is one absolutely essential feature not mentioned in F or N, and that is for automatic longitudinal stability *the two surfaces, the aerofoil proper and the balancer* (elevator or tail, or both), *must be separated by some considerable distance, a distance not less than four times the width of the main aerofoil.*[9] More is better.

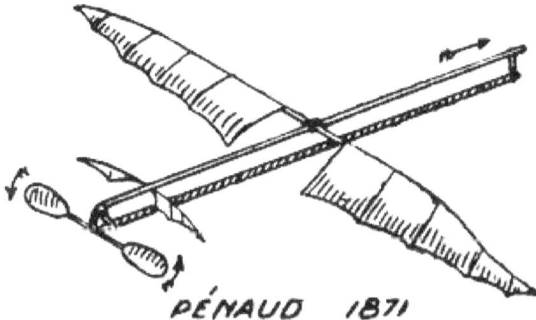

FIG. 7. PÉNAUD 1871

§ 7. With one exception (Pénaud) early experimenters with model aeroplanes had not grasped this all-important fact, and their models would not fly, only make a series of jumps, because they failed to balance longitudinally. In Stringfellow's and Tatin's models the main aerofoil and balancer (tail) are practically contiguous.

Pénaud in his rubber-motored models appears to have fully realised this (*vide* Fig. 7), and also the necessity for using long strands of rubber. Some of his models flew 150 ft., and showed considerable stability.

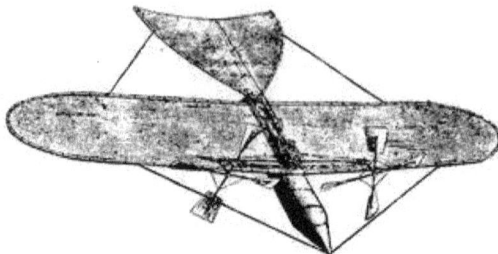

FIG. 8.—TATIN'S AEROPLANE (1879).
SURFACE 0·7 SQ. METRES, TOTAL WEIGHT 1·75 KILOGRAMMES,
VELOCITY OF SUSTENTATION 8 METRES A SECOND. MOTOR,
COMPRESSED AIR (FOR DESCRIPTION SEE § 23, CH. IV). REVOLVED
ROUND AND ROUND A TRACK TETHERED TO A POST AT THE CENTRE.
IN ONE OF ITS JUMPS IT CLEARED THE HEAD OF A SPECTATOR.

With three surfaces one would set the elevator at a slight plus angle, main aerofoil horizontal (neither positive nor negative), and the tail at a corresponding negative angle to the positive one of the elevator.

Referring to O.[10] One would naturally be inclined to put a keel surface—or, in other words, vertical fins—beneath the centre of gravity, but D shows us this may have the opposite effect to what we might expect.

In full-sized machines, those in which the distance between the main aerofoil and balancers is considerable (like the Farman) show considerable automatic longitudinal stability, and those in which it is short (like the Wright) are purposely made so with the idea of doing away with it, and rendering the machine quicker and more sensitive to personal control. In the case of the Stringfellow and Tatin models we have the extreme case—practically the bird entirely volitional and personal—which is the opposite in every way to what we desire on a model under no personal or volitional control at all.

FIG. 9.—CLARK'S MODEL FLYER.
MAIN AEROFOIL SET AT A SLIGHT NEGATIVE ANGLE. DIHEDRAL
ANGLES ON BOTH AEROFOILS.

The theoretical conditions stated in F and N are fully borne out in practice.

And since a curved aerofoil even when set at a *slight* negative angle has still considerable powers of sustentation, it is possible to give the main aerofoil a slight negative angle and the elevator a slight positive one. This fact is of the greatest importance, since it enables us to counteract the effect of the travel of the "centre of pressure."[11]

FIG. 10.—LARGE MODEL MONOPLANE,
DESIGNED AND CONSTRUCTED BY THE AUTHOR, WITH VERTICAL
FIN (NO DIHEDRAL ANGLE). WITH A LARGER AND MORE EFFICIENT
PROPELLER THAN THE ONE HERE SHOWN SOME EXCELLENT
FLIGHTS WERE OBTAINED. CONSTRUCTED OF BAMBOO AND
NAINSOOK. STAYED WITH STEEL WIRE.

§ 8. Referring to I. This, again, is of primary importance in longitudinal stability. The Farman machine has three such planes—elevator, main aerofoil, tail the Wright originally had *not*, but is now being fitted with a tail, and experiments on the Short-Wright biplane have quite proved its stabilising efficiency.

The three plane (triple monoplane) in the case of models has been tried, but possesses no advantage so far over the double monoplane type. The writer has made many experiments with vertical fins, and has found the machine very stable, even when the fin or vertical keel is placed some distance above the centre of gravity.

§ 9. The question of transverse (side to side) stability at once brings us to the question of the dihedral angle, practically similar in its action to a flat plane with vertical fins.

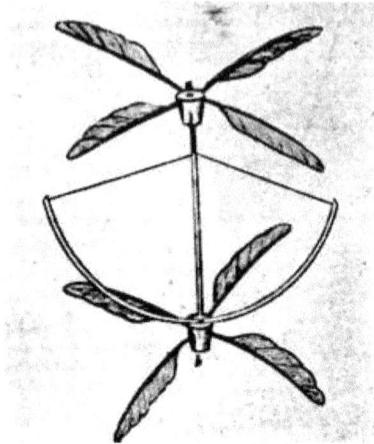

FIG. 11.—SIR GEORGE CAYLEY'S FLYING MACHINE.
EIGHT FEATHERS, TWO CORKS, A THIN ROD, A PIECE OF
WHALEBONE, AND A PIECE OF THREAD.

§ 10. The setting up of the front surface at an angle to the rear, or the setting of these at corresponding compensatory angles already dealt with, is nothing more nor less than the principle of the dihedral angle for longitudinal stability.

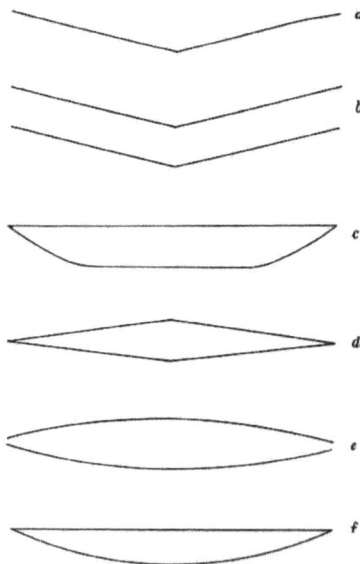

FIG. 12.—VARIOUS FORMS OF DIHEDRALS.

As early as the commencement of last century Sir George Cayley (a man more than a hundred years ahead of his times) was the first to point out that two planes at a dihedral angle constitute a basis of stability. For, on the machine heeling over, the side which is required to rise gains resistance by its new position, and that which is required to sink loses it.

§ 11. The dihedral angle principle may take many forms.

As in Fig. 12 *a* is a monoplane, the rest biplanes. The angles and curves are somewhat exaggerated. It is quite a mistake to make the angle excessive, the "lift" being thereby diminished. A few degrees should suffice.

Whilst it is evident enough that transverse stability is promoted by making the sustaining surface trough-shaped, it is not so evident what form of cross section is the most efficient for sustentation and equilibrium combined.

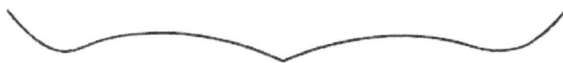

FIG. 13.

It is evident that the righting moment of a unit of surface of an aeroplane is greater at the outer edge than elsewhere, owing to the greater lever arm.

§ 12. The "upturned tip" dihedral certainly appears to have the advantage.

The outer edges of the aerofoil then should be turned upward for the purpose of transverse stability, while the inner surface should remain flat or concave for greater support.

§ 13. The exact most favourable outline of transverse section for stability, steadiness and buoyancy has not yet been found; but the writer has found the section given in Fig. 13, a very efficient one.

CHAPTER IV.
THE MOTIVE POWER.

§ 1. Some forty years have elapsed since Pénaud first used elastic (rubber) for model aeroplanes, and during that time no better substitute (in spite of innumerable experiments) has been found. Nor for the smaller and lighter class of models is there any likelihood of rubber being displaced. Such being the case, a brief account of some experiments on this substance as a motive power for the same may not be without interest. The word *elastic* (in science) denotes: *the tendency which a body has when distorted to return to its original shape.* Glass and ivory (within certain limits) are two of the most elastic bodies known. But the limits within which most bodies can be distorted (twisted or stretched, or both) without either fracture or a LARGE *permanent* alteration of shape is very small. Not so rubber—it far surpasses in this respect even steel springs.

§ 2. Let us take a piece of elastic (rubber) cord, and stretch it with known weights and observe carefully what happens. We shall find that, first of all: *the extension is proportional to the weight suspended*—but soon we have an *increasing* increase of extension. In one experiment made by the writer, when the weights were removed the rubber cord remained 1/8 of an inch longer, and at the end of an hour recovered itself to the extent of 1/16, remaining finally permanently 1/16 of an inch longer. Length of elastic cord used in this experiment 8-1/8 inches, 3/16 of an inch thick. Suspended weights, 1 oz. up to 64 oz. Extension from ¼ inch up to 24-5/8 inches. Graph drawn in Fig. 14, No. B abscissæ extension in eighths of an inch, ordinates weights in ounces. So long as the graph is a straight line it shows the extension is proportional to the suspended weight; afterwards in excess.

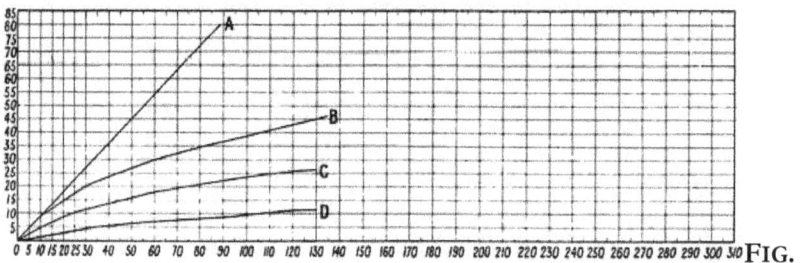

14.—WEIGHT AND EXTENSION.
B, rubber 3/16 in. thick; C, 2/16 in. thick; D, 1/16 in. thick. A, theoretical line if extension were proportional to weight.

In this experiment we have been able to stretch (distort) a piece of rubber to more than three times its original length, and afterwards it finally returns to almost its original length: not only so, a piece of rubber cord can be stretched to eight or nine times its original length without fracture. Herein lies its supreme advantage over steel or other springs. Weight for weight more energy can be got or more work be done by stretched (or twisted, or, to speak more correctly, by stretched-twisted) rubber cord than from any form of steel spring.[12] It is true it is stretched—twisted—far beyond what is called the "elastic limit," and its efficiency falls off, but with care not nearly so quickly as is commonly supposed, but in spite of this and other drawbacks its advantages far more than counterbalance these.

§ 3. Experimenting with cords of varying thickness we find that: *the extension is inversely proportional to the thickness.* If we leave a weight hanging on a piece of rubber cord (stretched, of course, beyond its "elastic limit") we find that: *the cord continues to elongate as long as the weight is left on.* For example: a 1 lb. weight hung on a piece of rubber cord, 8-1/8 inches long and 1/8 of an inch thick, stretched it—at first—6¼ inches; after two minutes this had increased to 6-5/8 (3/8 of an inch more). One hour later 1/8 of an inch more, and sixteen hours later 1/8 of an inch more, i.e. a sixteen hours' hang produced an additional extension of ¾ of an inch. On a thinner cord (half the thickness) same weight produced *an additional extension (after 14 hours) of* 10-3/8 *in.*

N.B.—An elastic cord or spring balance should never have a weight left permanently on it—or be subjected to a distorting force for a longer time than necessary, or it will take a "permanent set," and not return to even approximately its original length or form.

In a rubber cord the extension is *directly proportional to the length* as well as *inversely proportional to the thickness and to the weight suspended*—true only within the limits of elasticity.

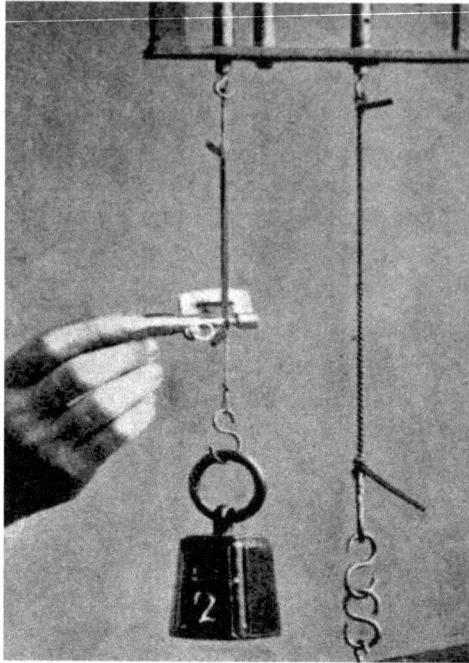

FIG. 15.—EXTENSION AND INCREASE IN VOLUME.

§ 4. **When a Rubber Cord is stretched there is an Increase of Volume.**—
On stretching a piece of rubber cord to *twice* its original (natural) length, we should perhaps expect to find that the string would only be *half* as thick, as would be the case if the volume remained the same. Performing the experiment, and measuring the cord as accurately as possible with a micrometer, measuring to the one-thousandth of an inch, we at once perceive that this is not the case, being about *two-thirds* of its former volume.

§ 5. In the case of rubber cord used for a motive power on model aeroplanes, the rubber is *both* twisted and stretched, but chiefly the latter.

Thirty-six strands of rubber, weight about 56 grammes, at 150 turns give a torque of 4 oz. on a 5-in. arm, but an end thrust, or end pull, of about 3½ lb. (Ball bearings, or some such device, can be used to obviate this end thrust when desirable.) A series of experiments undertaken by the writer on the torque produced by twisted rubber strands, varying in number, length, etc., and afterwards carefully plotted out in graph form, have led to some very interesting and instructive results. Ball bearings were used, and the torque, measured in eighths of an ounce, was taken (in each case) from an arm 5 in. in length.

The following are the principal results arrived at. For graphs, see Fig. 16.

§ 6. A. Increasing the number of (rubber) strands by *one-half* (length and thickness of rubber remaining constant) increases the torque (unwinding tendency) *twofold*, i.e., doubles the motive power.

B. *Doubling* the number of strands increases the torque *more than three times*— about 3-1/3 times, 3 times up to 100 turns, 3½ times from 100 to 250 turns.

C. *Trebling* the number of strands increases the torque at least *seven times*.

The increased *size* of the coils, and thereby *increased* extension, explains this result. As we increase the number of strands, the *number* of twists or turns that can be given it becomes less.

D. *Doubling* the number of strands (length, etc., remaining constant) *diminishes* the number of turns by *one-third to one-half*. (In few strands one-third, in 30 and over one-half.)

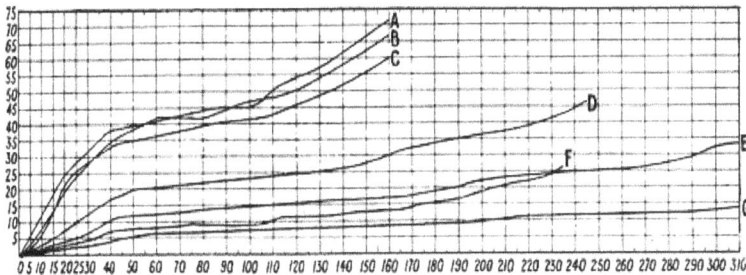

FIG. 16.—TORQUE GRAPHS OF RUBBER MOTORS.

Abscissæ = Turns.

Ordinates = Torque measured in 1/16 of an oz. Length of arm, 5 in.

A. 38 strands of new rubber, 2 ft. 6 in. long; 58 grammes weight.

B. 36 strands, 2 ft. 6 in. long; end thrust at 150 turns, 3½ lb.

C. 32 strands, 2 ft. 6 in. long.

D. 24 "" "

E. 18 " " "   weight 28 grammes.

F. 12 " 1 ft. 3 in. long

G. 12 " 2 ft. 6 in. long.

E. If we halve the length of the rubber strands, keeping the *number* of strands the same, the torque is but slightly increased for the first 100 turns; at 240 turns it is double. But the greater number of turns—in ratio of about 2:1— that can be given the longer strand much more than compensates for this.

F. No arrangement of the strands, *per se*, gets more energy (more motive power) out of them than any other, but there are special reasons for making the strands—

G. As long and as few in number as possible.

1. More turns can be given it.

2. It gives a far more even torque. Twelve strands 2 ft. 6 in. long give practically a line of small constant angle. Thirty-six strands same length a much steeper angle, with considerable variations.

A very good result, which the writer has verified in practice, paying due regard to *both* propeller and motor, is to make—

H. *The length of the rubber strands twice*[13] *in feet the number of the strands in inches,*[14] e.g., if the number of strands is 12 their length should be 2 ft., if 18, 3 ft., and so on.

§ 7. Experiments with 32 to 38 strands 2 ft. 6 in. long give a torque curve almost precisely similar to that obtained from experiments made with flat spiral steel springs, similar to those used in watches and clocks; and, as we know, the torque given by such springs is very uneven, and has to be equalised by use of a fusee, or some such device. In the case of such springs it must not be forgotten that the turning moment (unwinding tendency) is NOT proportional to the amount of winding up, this being true only in the "balance" springs of watches, etc., where *both* ends of the spring are rigidly fastened.

In the case of SPRING MOTORS.[15]

I. The turning moment (unwinding tendency) is proportional to the difference between the angle of winding and yielding, proportional to the moment of inertia of its section, i.e., to the breadth and the cube of its thickness, also proportional to the modulus of elasticity of the substance used, and inversely proportional to the length of the strip.

§ 8. Referring back to A, B, C, there are one or two practical deductions which should be carefully noted.

Supposing we have a model with one propeller and 36 strands of elastic. If we decide to fit it with twin screws, then, other reasons apart, we shall require two sets of strands of more than 18 in number each to have the same motive power (27 if the same torque be required).[16] This is an important point, and one not to be lost sight of when thinking of using two propellers.

Experiments on—

§9. **The Number of Revolutions** (turns) **that can be given to Rubber Motors** led to interesting results, e.g., the number of turns to produce a double knot in the cord from end to end were, in the case of rubber, one yard long:—

No. of Strands.	No. of Turns.	No. of Strands.	No. of Turns.
4	440	16	200
8	310	28	170
12	250		

It will be at once noticed that the greater the number of rubber strands used in a given length, the fewer turns will it stand in proportion. For instance, 8 strands double knot at 310, and 4 at 440 (and not at 620), 16 at 200, and 8 at 310 (and not 400), and so on. The reason, of course, is the more the strands the greater the distance they have to travel round themselves.

§ 10. **The Maximum Number of Turns.**—As to the maximum number of permissible turns, rubber has rupture stress of 330 lb. per sq. in., *but a very high permissible stress*, as much as 80 per cent. The resilience (power of recovery after distortion) in tension of rubber is in considerable excess of any other substance, silk being the only other substance which at all approaches it in this respect, the ratio being about 11 : 9. The resilience of steel spiral spring is very slight in comparison.

A rubber motor in which the double knot is not exceeded by more than 100 turns (rubber one yard in length) should last a good time. When trying for a record flight, using new elastic, as many as even 500 or 600 or even more turns have been given in the case of 32-36 strands a yard in length; but such a severe strain soon spoils the rubber.

§ 11. **On the Use of "Lubricants."**—One of the drawbacks to rubber is that if it be excessively strained it soon begins to break up. One of the chief causes of this is that the strands stick together—they should always be carefully separated, if necessary, after a flight—and an undue strain is thereby cast on certain parts. Apart also from this the various strands are not subject to the same tension. It has been suggested that if some means could be devised to prevent this, and allow the strands to slip over one another, a considerable increase of power might result. It must, however, be carefully borne in mind that anything of an oily or greasy nature has an injurious effect on the rubber, and must be avoided at all costs. Benzol, petroleum, ether, volatile oils, turpentine, chloroform, naphtha, vaseline, soap, and all kinds of oil must be carefully avoided, as they soften the rubber, and reduce it more or less to the consistence of a sticky mass. The only oil which is said to have no action on rubber, or practically none, is castor oil; all the same, I do not advise its use as a lubricant.

There are three only which we need consider:—

- 1. Soda and water.
- 2. French chalk.
- 3. Pure redistilled glycerine.

The first is perfectly satisfactory when freshly applied, but soon dries up and evaporates.

The second falls off; and unless the chalk be of the softest kind, free from all grit and hard particles, it will soon do more harm than good.

The third, glycerine, is for ordinary purposes by far the best, and has a beneficial rather than a deleterious effect on the rubber; but it must be *pure*. The redistilled kind, free from all traces of arsenic, grease, etc., is the only kind permissible. It does not evaporate, and a few drops, comparatively speaking, will lubricate fifty or sixty yards of rubber.

Being of a sticky or tacky nature it naturally gathers up dust and particles of dirt in course of time. To prevent these grinding into the rubber, wash it from time to time in warm soda, and warm and apply fresh glycerine when required.

Glycerine, unlike vaseline (a product of petroleum), is not a grease; it is formed from fats by a process known as *saponification*, or treatment of the oil with caustic alkali, which decomposes the compound, forming an alkaline stearate (soap), and liberating the glycerine which remains in solution when the soap is separated by throwing in common salt. In order to obtain pure glycerine, the fat can be decomposed by lead oxide, the glycerine remaining in solution, and the lead soap or plaster being precipitated.

By using glycerine as a lubricant the number of turns that can be given a rubber motor is greatly increased, and the coils slip over one another freely and easily, and prevent the throwing of undue strain on some particular portion, and absolutely prevent the strands from sticking together.

§ 12. **The Action of Copper upon Rubber.**—Copper, whether in the form of the metal, the oxides, or the soluble salts, has a marked injurious action upon rubber.

In the case of metallic copper this action has been attributed to oxidation induced by the dissolved oxygen in the copper. In working drawings for model aeroplanes I have noticed designs in which the hooks on which the rubber strands were to be stretched were made of *copper*. In no case should the strands be placed upon bare metal. I always cover mine with a piece of valve tubing, which can easily be renewed from time to time.

§ 12A. **The Action of Water, etc., on Rubber.**—Rubber is quite insoluble in water; but it must not be forgotten that it will absorb about 25 per cent. into its pores after soaking for some time.

Ether, chloroform, carbon-tetrachloride, turpentine, carbon bi-sulphide, petroleum spirit, benzene and its homologues found in coal-tar naphtha, dissolve rubber readily. Alcohol is absorbed by rubber, but is not a solvent of it.

§ 12B. **How to Preserve Rubber.**—In the first place, in order that it shall be *possible* to preserve and keep rubber in the best condition of efficiency, it is absolutely essential that the rubber shall be, when obtained, fresh and of the best kind. Only the best Para rubber should be bought; to obtain it fresh it should be got in as large quantities as possible direct from a manufacturer or reliable rubber shop. The composition of the best Para rubber is as follows:—Carbon, 87·46 per cent.; hydrogen, 12·00 per cent.; oxygen and ash, 0·54 per cent.

In order to increase its elasticity the pure rubber has to be vulcanised before being made into the sheet some sixty or eighty yards in length, from which the rubber threads are cut; after vulcanization the substance consists of rubber plus about 3 per cent. of sulphur. Now, unfortunately, the presence of the sulphur makes the rubber more prone to atmospheric oxidation. Vulcanized rubber, compared to pure rubber, has then but a limited life. It is to this process of oxidation that the more or less rapid deterioration of rubber is due.

To preserve rubber it should be kept from the sun's rays, or, indeed, any actinic rays, in a cool, airy place, and subjected to as even a temperature as possible. Great extremes of temperature have a very injurious effect on rubber, and it should be washed from time to time in warm soda water. It should be subjected to no tension or compression.

Deteriorated rubber is absolutely useless for model aeroplanes.

§ 13. **To Test Rubber.**—Good elastic thread composed of pure Para rubber and sulphur should, if properly made, stretch to seven times its length, and then return to its original length. It should also possess a stretching limit at least ten times its original length.

As already stated, the threads or strands are cut from sheets; these threads can now be cut fifty to the inch. For rubber motors a very great deal so far as length of life depends on the accuracy and skill with which the strands are cut. When examined under a microscope (not too powerful) the strands having the least ragged edge, i.e., the best cut, are to be preferred.

§ 14. **The Section—Strip or Ribbon versus Square.**—In section the square and not the ribbon or strip should be used. The edge of the strip I have always found more ragged under the microscope than the square. I have also found it less efficient. Theoretically no doubt a round section would be best, but none such (in small sizes) is on the market. Models have been fitted with a tubular section, but such should on no account be used.

§ 15. **Size of the Section.**—One-sixteenth or one-twelfth is the best size for ordinary models; personally, I prefer the thinner. If more than a certain number of strands are required to provide the necessary power, a larger size should be used. It is not easy to say *what* this number is, but fifty may probably be taken as an outside limit. Remember the size increases by area section; twice the *sectional* height and breadth means four times the rubber.

§ 16. **Geared Rubber Motors.**—It is quite a mistake to suppose that any advantage can be obtained by using a four to one gearing, say; all that you do obtain is one-fourth of the power minus the increased friction, minus the added weight. This presumes, of course, you make no alteration in your rubber strands.

Gearing such as this means *short* rubber strands, and such are not to be desired; in any case, there is the difficulty of increased friction and added weight to overcome. It is true by splitting up your rubber motor into two sets of strands instead of one you can obtain more turns, but, as we have seen, you must increase the number of strands to get the same thrust, and you have this to counteract any advantage you gain as well as added weight and friction.

§ 17. The writer has tried endless experiments with all kinds of geared rubber motors, and the only one worth a moment's consideration is the following, viz., one in which two gear wheels—same size, weight, and number of teeth—are made use of, the propeller being attached to the axle of one of them, and the same number of strands are used on each axle. The success or non-success of this motor depends entirely on the method used in its construction. At first sight it may appear that no great skill is required in the construction of such a simple piece of apparatus. No greater mistake could be made. It is absolutely necessary that *the friction and weight be reduced to a minimum*, and the strength be a maximum. The torque of the rubber strands on so short an arm is very great.

Ordinary light brass cogwheels will not stand the strain.

A. The cogwheels should be of steel[17] and accurately cut of diameter sufficient to separate the two strands the requisite distance, *but no more.*

B. The weight must be a minimum. This is best attained by using solid wheels, and lightening by drilling and turning.

C. The friction must be a minimum. Use the lightest ball bearings obtainable (these weigh only 0·3 gramme), adjust the wheels so that they run with the greatest freedom, but see that the teeth overlap sufficiently to stand the strain and slight variations in direction without fear of slipping. Shallow teeth are useless.

D. Use vaseline on the cogs to make them run as easily as possible.

FIG. 17.—GEARED RUBBER MOTOR.
DESIGNED AND CONSTRUCTED BY THE WRITER. FOR DESCRIPTION OF THE MODEL, ETC., SEE APPENDIX.

E. The material of the containing framework must be of maximum strength and minimum lightness. Construct it of minimum size, box shaped, use the thinnest tin (really tinned sheet-iron) procurable, and lighten by drilling holes, not too large, all over it. Do not use aluminium or magnalium. Steel, could it be procured thin enough, would be better still.

F. Use steel pianoforte wire for the spindles, and hooks for the rubber strands, using as thin wire as will stand the strain.

Unless these directions are carefully carried out no advantage will be gained—the writer speaks from experience. The requisite number of rubber strands to give the best result must be determined by experiment.

§ 18. One advantage in using such a motor as this is that the two equal strands untwisting in opposite directions have a decided steadying effect on the model, similar almost to the case in which two propellers are used.

The "best" model flights that the writer has achieved have been obtained with a motor of this description.[18]

In the case of twin screws two such gearings can be used, and the rubber split up into four strands. The containing framework in this case can be simply light pieces of tubing let into the wooden framework, or very light iron pieces fastened thereto.

Do not attempt to split up the rubber into more than two strands to each propeller.

SECTION II.—OTHER FORMS OF MOTORS.

§ 18A. **Spring Motors.**—This question has already been dealt with more or less whilst dealing with rubber motors, and the superiority of the latter over the former pointed out. Rubber has a much greater superiority over steel or other springs, because in stretch-twisted rubber far more energy can be stored up weight for weight. One pound weight of elastic can be made to store up some 320 ft.-lb. of energy, and steel only some 65 lb. And in addition to this there is the question of gearing, involving extra weight and friction; that is, if flat steel springs similar to those used in clockwork mechanism be made use of, as is generally the case. The only instance in which such springs are of use is for the purpose of studying the effects of different distributions of weight on the model, and its effect on the balance of the machine; but effects such as this can be brought about without a change of motor.

§ 18B. A more efficient form of spring motor, doing away with gearing troubles, is to use a long spiral spring (as long as the rubber strands) made of medium-sized piano wire, similar in principle to those used in some roller-blinds, but longer and of thinner steel.

The writer has experimented with such, as well as scores of other forms of spring motors, but none can compare with rubber.

The long spiral form of steel spring is, however, much the best.

§ 18C. **Compressed Air Motors.**—This is a very fascinating form of motor, on paper, and appears at first sight the ideal form. It is so easy to write: "Its weight is negligible, and it can be provided free of cost; all that is necessary is to work a bicycle pump for as many minutes as the motor is desired to run.

This stored-up energy can be contained in a mere tube, of aluminium or magnalium, forming the central rib of the machine, and the engine mechanism necessary for conveying this stored-up energy to the revolving propeller need weigh only a few ounces." Another writer recommends "a pressure of 300 lb."

§ 18D. A pneumatic drill generally works at about 80 lb. pressure, and when developing 1 horse-power, uses about 55 cubic ft. of free air per minute. Now if we apply this to a model aeroplane of average size, taking a reservoir 3 ft. long by 1½ in. internal diameter, made of magnalium, say—steel would, of course, be much better—the weight of which would certainly not be less than 4 oz., we find that at 80 lb. pressure such a motor would use

$$55 \text{ / Horse Power (H.P.)}$$

cub. ft. per minute.

Now 80 lb. is about 5½ atmospheres, and the cubical contents of the above motor some 63 cub. in. The time during which such a model would fly depends on the H.P. necessary for flight; but a fair allowance gives a flight of from 10 to 30 sec. I take 80 lb. pressure as a fair practical limit.

§ 18E. The pressure in a motor-car tyre runs from 40 to 80 lb., usually about 70 lb. Now 260 strokes are required with an ordinary inflator to obtain so low a pressure as 70 lb., and it is no easy job, as those who have done it know.

§ 19. Prior to 1893 Mr. Hargraves (of cellular kite fame) studied the question of compressed-air motors for model flying machines. His motor was described as a marvel of simplicity and lightness, its cylinder was made like a common tin can, the cylinder covers cut from sheet tin and pressed to shape, the piston and junk rings of ebonite.

One of his receivers was 23-3/8 in. long, and 5·5 in. diameter, of aluminium plate 0·2 in. thick, 3/8 in. by 1/8 in. riveting strips were insufficient to make tight joints; it weighed 26 oz., and at 80 lb. water pressure one of the ends blew out, the fracture occurring at the bend of the flange, and not along the line of rivets. The receiver which was successful being apparently a tin-iron one; steel tubing was not to be had at that date in Sydney. With a receiver of this character, and the engine referred to above, a flight of 343 ft. was obtained, this flight being the best. (The models constructed by him were not on the aeroplane, but ornithoptere, or wing-flapping principle.) The time of flight was 23 *seconds*, with 54½ double vibrations of the engines. The efficiency of this motor was estimated to be 29 per cent.

§ 20. By using compressed air, and heating it in its passage to the cylinder, far greater efficiency can be obtained. Steel cylinders can be obtained containing air under the enormous pressure of 120 atmospheres.[19] This is practically liquid air. A 20-ft. cylinder weighs empty 23 lb. The smaller the cylinder the less the proportionate pressure that it will stand; and supposing a small steel cylinder, produced of suitable form and weight, and capable of withstanding with safety a pressure of from 300 to 600 lb. per sq. in., or from 20 to 40 atmospheres. The most economical way of working would be to admit the air from the reservoir directly to the motor cylinders; but this would mean a very great range in the initial working pressure, entailing not-to-be-thought-of weight in the form of multi-cylinder compound engines, variable expansion gear, etc.

§ 21. This means relinquishing the advantages of the high initial pressure, and the passing of the air through a reducing valve, whereby a constant pressure, say, of 90 to 150, according to circumstances, could be maintained. By a variation in the ratio of expansion the air could be worked down to, say, 30 lb.

The initial loss entailed by the use of a reducing valve may be in a great measure restored by heating the air before using it in the motor cylinders; by heating it to a temperature of only 320°F., by means of a suitable burner, the volume of air is increased by one half, the consumption being reduced in the same proportion; the consumption of air used in this way being 24 lb. per indicated horse-power per hour. But this means extra weight in the form of fuel and burners, and what we gain in one way we lose in another. It is, of course, desirable that the motor should work at as low a pressure as possible, since as the store of air is used up the pressure in the reservoir falls, until it reaches a limit below which it cannot usefully be employed. The air then remaining is dead and useless, adding only to the weight of the aeroplane.

§ 22. From calculations made by the writer the *entire* weight of a compressed-air model motor plant would be at least *one-third* the weight of the aeroplane, and on a small scale probably one-half, and cannot therefore hold comparison with the *steam engine* discussed in the next paragraph. In concluding these remarks on compressed-air motors, I do not wish to dissuade anyone from trying this form of motor; but they must not embark on experiments with the idea that anything useful or anything superior to results obtained with infinitely less expense by means of rubber can be brought to pass with a bicycle pump, a bit of magnalium tube, and 60 lb. pressure.

§ 22A. In Tatin's air-compressed motor the reservoir weighed 700 grammes, and had a capacity of 8 litres. It was tested to withstand a pressure of 20 atmospheres, but was worked only up to seven. The little engine attached thereto weighed 300 grammes, and developed a motive power of 2 kilogram-metres per second (*see* ch. iii.).

§ 23. **Steam-Driven Motors.**—Several successful steam-engined model aeroplanes have been constructed, the most famous being those of Professor Langley.

Having constructed over 30 modifications of rubber-driven models, and experimented with compressed air, carbonic-acid gas, electricity, and other methods of obtaining energy, he finally settled upon the steam engine (the petrol motor was not available at that time, 1893). After many months' work it was found that the weight could not be reduced below 40 lb., whilst the engine would only develop ½ H.P., and finally the model was condemned. A second apparatus to be worked by compressed air was tried, but the power proved insufficient. Then came another with a carbonic-acid gas engine. Then others with various applications of electricity and gas, etc., but the steam engine was found most suitable; yet it seemed to become more and more doubtful whether it could ever be made sufficiently light, and whether the desired end could be attained at all. The chief obstacle proved not to be with the engines, which were made surprisingly light after sufficient experiment. *The great difficulty was to make a boiler of almost no weight which would give steam enough.*

§ 24. At last a satisfactory boiler and engine were produced.

The engine was of 1 to 1½ H.P., total weight (including moving parts) 26 oz. The cylinders, two in number, had each a diameter of 1¼ in., and piston stroke 2 in.

The boiler, with its firegrate, weighed a little over 5 lb. It consisted of a continuous helix of copper tubing, 3/8 in. external diameter, the diameter of the coil being 3 in. altogether. Through the centre of this was driven the blast from an "Ælopile," a modification of the naphtha blow-torch used by plumbers, the flame of which is about 2000° F.[20] The pressure of steam issuing into the engines varied from 100 to 150 lb. per sq. in.; 4 lb. weight of water and about 10 oz. of naphtha could be carried. The boiler evaporated 1 lb. of water per minute.

The twin propellers, 39 in. in diam., pitch 1¼, revolved from 800 to 1000 a minute. The entire aeroplane was 15 ft. in length, the aerofoils from tip to tip about 14 ft., and the total weight slightly less than 30 lb., of which *one-fourth was contained in the machinery.* Its flight was a little over half a mile in length, and of 1½ minutes' duration. Another model flew for about three-quarters of a mile, at a rate of about 30 miles an hour.

It will be noted that engine, generator, etc., work out at about 7 lb. per H.P. Considerable advance has been made in the construction of light and powerful model steam engines since Langley's time, chiefly in connexion with model hydroplanes, and a pressure of from 500 to 600 lb. per sq. in. has been employed; the steam turbine has been brought to a high state of perfection, and it is now possible to make a model De Laval turbine of considerable power weighing almost next to nothing,[21] the real trouble, in fact the only one, being the steam generator. An economization of weight means a waste of steam, of which models can easily spend their only weight in five minutes.

§ 25. One way to economize without increased weight in the shape of a condenser is to use spirit (methylated spirit, for instance) for both fuel and boiler, and cause the exhaust from the engines to be ejected on to the burning spirit, where it itself serves as fuel. By using spirit, or some very volatile hydrocarbon, instead of water, we have a further advantage from the fact that such vaporize at a much lower temperature than water.

§ 26. When experimenting with an engine of the turbine type we must use a propeller of small diameter and pitch, owing to the very high velocity at which such engines run.

Anyone, however, who is not an expert on such matters would do well to leave such motors alone, as the very highest technical skill, combined with many preliminary disappointments and trials, are sure to be encountered before success is attained.

§ 27. And the smaller the model the more difficult the problem—halve your aeroplane, and your difficulties increase anything from fourfold to tenfold.

The boiler would in any case be of the flash type of either copper or steel tubing (the former for safety), with a magnalium container for the spirit, and a working pressure of from 150 to 200 lb. per sq. in. Anything less than this would not be worth consideration.

§ 28. Some ten months after Professor Langley's successful model flights (1896), experiments were made in France at Carquenez, near Toulon. The total weight of the model aeroplane in this case was 70 lb.; the engine power a little more than 1 H.P. Twin screws were used—*one in front and one behind.* The maximum velocity obtained was 40 miles per hour; but the length of run only 154 yards, and duration of flight only a few seconds. This result compares very poorly with Langley's distance (of best flight), nearly one mile, duration 1 min. 45 sec. The maximum velocity was greater—30 to 40 miles per hour. The total breadth of this large model was rather more than 6 metres, and the surface a little more than 8 sq. metres.

§ 29. **Petrol Motors.**—Here it would appear at first thought is the true solution of the problem of the model aeroplane motor. Such a motor has solved the problem of aerial locomotion, as the steam engine solved that of terrestrial and marine travel, both full sized and model; and if in the case of full sized machines, then why not models.

Fig. 18.—Mr. Stanger's Model in Full Flight.

FIG. 19.—MR. STANGER'S PETROL-DRIVEN MODEL AEROPLANE.
[ILLUSTRATIONS BY PERMISSION FROM ELECTROS SUPPLIED BY THE
"AERO."]

§ 30. The exact size of the smallest *working* model steam engine that has been made I do not know,[22] but it is or could be surprisingly small; not so the petrol motor—not one, that is, that would *work*. The number of petrol motor-driven model aeroplanes that have actually flown is very small. Personally I only know of one, viz., Mr. D. Stanger's, exhibited at the aero exhibition at the Agricultural Hall in 1908.

Fig. 20.—Mr. Stanger's Model Petrol Engine.

FIG. 21.—MR. STANGER'S MODEL PETROL ENGINE.

In Fig. 21 the motor is in position on the aeroplane. Note small carburettor. In Fig. 20 an idea of the size of engine may be gathered by comparing it with the ordinary sparking-plug seen by the side, whilst to the left of this is one of the special plugs used on this motor.

(Illustrations by permission from electros supplied by the "Aero.")

§ 31. The following are the chief particulars of this interesting machine:— The engine is a four-cylinder one, and weighs (complete with double carburetter and petrol tank) 5½ lb., and develops 1¼ H.P. at 1300 revolutions per minute.

FIG. 22.—ONE-CYLINDER PETROL MOTOR.
(Electro from Messrs. A.W. Gamage's Aviation Catalogue.)

The propeller, 29 in. in diam. and 36 in. in pitch, gives a static thrust of about 7 lb. The machine has a spread of 8 ft. 2 in., and is 6 ft. 10 in. in length. Total weight 21 lb. Rises from the ground when a speed of about 16 miles an hour is attained. A clockwork arrangement automatically stops the engine. The engine air-cooled. The cylinder of steel, cast-iron heads, aluminium crank-case, double float feed carburetter, ignition by single coil and distributor. The aeroplane being 7 ft. 6 in. long, and having a span 8 ft.

§ 32. **One-cylinder Petrol Motors.**—So far as the writer is aware no success has as yet attended the use of a single-cylinder petrol motor on a model aeroplane. Undoubtedly the vibration is excessive; but this should not be an insuperable difficulty. It is true it is heavier in proportion than a two-cylinder one, and not so efficient; and so far has not proved successful. The question of vibration on a model aeroplane is one of considerable importance. A badly balanced propeller even will seriously interfere with and often greatly curtail the length of flight.

§ 33. **Electric Motors.**—No attempt should on any account be made to use electric motors for model aeroplanes. They are altogether too heavy, apart even from the accumulator or source of electric energy, for the power derivable from them. To take an extreme case, and supposing we use a 2-oz. electric motor capable of driving a propeller giving a static thrust of 3 oz.,[23] on weighing one of the smallest size accumulators without case, etc., I find its weight is 4½ oz. One would, of course, be of no use; at least three would be required, and they would require practically short circuiting to give sufficient amperage (running them down, that is, in some 10 to 15 seconds). Total weight, 1 lb. nearly. Now from a *pound* weight of rubber one could obtain a thrust of *pounds*, not ounces. For scale models not intended for actual flight, of course, electric motors have their uses.

CHAPTER V.

PROPELLERS OR SCREWS.

§ 1. The design and construction of propellers, more especially the former, is without doubt one of the most difficult parts of model aeroplaning.

With elastic or spring driven models the problem is more complicated than for models driven by petrol or some vaporized form of liquid fuel; and less reliable information is to hand. The problem of *weight*, unfortunately, is of primary importance.

We will deal with these points in due course; to begin with let us take:—

THE POSITION OF THE PROPELLER.

In model aeroplanes the propeller is usually situated either in front or in the rear of the model; in the former case it is called a TRACTOR SCREW, i.e., it pulls instead of pushes.

As to the merits of the two systems with respect to the tractor, there is, we know, in the case of models moving through water a distinct advantage in placing the propeller behind, and using a pushing or propulsive action, on account of the frictional "wake" created behind the boat, and which causes the water to flow after the vessel, but at a lesser velocity.

In placing the propeller behind, we place it in such a position as to act upon and make use of this phenomenon, the effect of the propeller being to bring this following wake to rest. Theoretically a boat, model or otherwise, can be propelled with less horse-power than it can be towed. But with respect to aeroplanes, apart altogether from the difference of medium, there is *at present* a very considerable difference of *form*, an aeroplane, model or otherwise, bearing at present but little resemblance to the hull of a boat.

Undoubtedly there is a frictional wake in the case of aeroplanes, possibly quite as much in proportion as in the case of a boat, allowing for difference of medium. Admitting, then, that this wake does exist, it follows that a propulsive screw is better than a tractor. In a matter of this kind constructional considerations, or "ease of launching," and "ability to land without damage," must be given due weight.

In the case of model aeroplanes constructional details incline the balance neither one way nor the other; but "ease in launching" and "ability to land without damage" weigh the balance down most decidedly in favour of a driving or propulsive screw.

In the case of full-sized monoplanes constructional details had most to do with the use of tractors; but monoplanes are now being built with propulsive screws.[24]

In the case of models, not models of full-sized machines, but actual model flyers, the writer considers propulsive screws much the best.[25]

In no case should the propeller be placed in the centre of the model, or in such a position as to *shorten the strands of the elastic motor*, if good flights are desired.

In the case of petrol or similar driven models the position of the propeller can be safely copied from actual well-recognised and successful full-sized machines.

§ 2. **The Number of Blades.**—Theoretically the number of blades does not enter into consideration. The mass of air dealt with by the propeller is represented by a cylinder of indefinite length, whose diameter is the same as that of the screw, and the rate at which this cylinder is projected to the rear depends theoretically upon the pitch and revolutions (per minute, say) of the propeller and not the number of blades. Theoretically one blade (helix incomplete) would be sufficient, but such a screw would not "balance," and balance is of primary importance; the minimum number of blades which can be used is therefore *two*.

In marine models three blades are considered best, as giving a better balance.

In the case of their aerial prototypes the question of *weight* has again to be considered, and two blades is practically the invariable custom.[26] Here, again, constructional considerations again come to the fore, and in the case of wooden propellers one of two blades is of far more easy construction than one of three.

By increasing the number of blades the "thrust" is, of course, more evenly distributed over a larger area, but the weight is considerably increased, and in models a greater advantage is gained by keeping down the weight than might follow from the use of more blades.

§ 3. **Fan versus Propeller.**—It must always be most carefully borne in mind that a fan (ventilating) and a propeller are not the same thing. Because many blades are found in practice to be efficient in the case of the former, it is quite wrong to assume that the same conclusion holds in the case of the latter.

By increasing the number of blades the skin friction due to the resistance that has to be overcome in rotating the propeller through the air is added to.

Moreover a fan is stationary, whilst a propeller is constantly *advancing* as well as *rotating* through the air.

The action of a fan blower is to move a small quantity of air at a high velocity; whereas the action of a propeller is, or should be, to move *a large quantity of air at a small velocity*, for the function of a screw is to create thrust. Operating on a yielding fluid medium this thrust will evidently be in proportion to the mass of fluid moved, and also to the velocity at which it is put in motion.

But the power consumed in putting this mass of fluid in motion is proportional to the mass and to the *square* of the velocity at which it moves. From this it follows, as stated above, that in order to obtain a given thrust with the least loss of power, the mass of fluid acted on should be as large as possible, and the velocity imparted to it as little as possible.

A fan requires to be so designed as to create a thrust when stationary (static thrust), and a propeller whilst moving through the air (dynamic thrust).

§ 4. **The Function of a Propeller** is to produce dynamic thrust; and the great advantage of the use of a propeller as a thrusting or propulsive agent is that its surface is always active. It has no *dead* points, and its motion is continuous and not reciprocating, and it requires no special machinery or moving parts in its construction and operation.

§ 5. **The Pitch** of a propeller or screw is the linear distance a screw moves, backwards or forwards, in one complete revolution. This distance is purely a theoretical one. When, for instance, a screw is said to have a pitch of 1 ft., or 12 in., it means that the model would advance 1 ft. through the air for each revolution of the screw, provided that the propeller blade were mounted in *solid* guides, like a nut on a bolt with one thread per foot. In a yielding fluid such as water or air it does not practically advance this distance, and hence occurs what is known as—

§ 6. **Slip**, which may be defined as the distance which ought to be traversed, but which is lost through imperfections in the propelling mechanism; or it may be considered as power which should have been used in driving the model forward. In the case of a locomotive running on dry rails nothing is lost in slip, there being none. In the case of a steamer moored and her engines set going, or of an aeroplane held back prior to starting, all the power is used in slip, i.e. in putting the fluid in motion, and none is used in propulsion.

Supposing the propeller on our model has a pitch of 1 ft., and we give the elastic motor 100 turns, theoretically the model should travel 100 ft. in calm air before the propeller is run down; no propeller yet designed will do this. Supposing the actual length 77 ft., 23 per cent. has been lost in "slip." For this to be actually correct the propeller must stop at the precise instant when the machine comes to ground.

Taking "slip" into account, then—

The speed of the model in feet per minute = pitch (in feet) × revolutions per minute— slip (feet per minute).

This slip wants to be made small—just how small is not yet known.

If made too small then the propeller will not be so efficient, or, at any rate, such is the conclusion come to in marine propulsion, where it is found for the most economical results to be obtained that the slip should be from 10 to 20 per cent.

In the case of aerial propellers a slip of 25 per cent. is quite good, 40 per cent. bad; and there are certain reasons for assuming that possibly about 15 per cent. may be the best.

§ 7. It is true that slip represents energy lost; but some slip is essential, because without slip there could be no "thrust," this same thrust being derived from the reaction of the volume of air driven backwards.

The thrust is equal to—

Weight of mass of air acted on per second × slip velocity in feet per second.

In the case of an aeroplane advancing through the air it might be thought that the thrust would be less. Sir Hiram Maxim found, however, as the result of his experiments that the thrust with a propeller travelling through the air at a velocity of 40 miles an hour was the same as when stationary, the r.p.m. remaining constant throughout. The explanation is that when travelling the propeller is continually advancing on to "undisturbed" air, the "slip" velocity is reduced, but the undisturbed air is equivalent to acting upon a greater mass of air.

§ 8. **Pitch Coefficient or Pitch Ratio.**—If we divide the pitch of a screw by its diameter we obtain what is known as pitch coefficient or ratio.

The mean value of eighteen pitch coefficients of well-known full-sized machines works out at $0·62$, which, as it so happens, is exactly the same as the case of the Farman machine propeller considered alone, this ratio varying from $0·4$ to $1·2$; in the case of the Wright's machine it is (probably) 1. The efficiency of their propeller is admitted on all hands. Their propeller is, of course, a slow-speed propeller, 450 r.p.m. The one on the Blériot monoplane (Blériot XI.) pitch ratio $0·4$, r.p.m. 1350.

In marine propulsion the pitch ratio is generally $1·3$ for a slow-speed propeller, decreasing to $0·9$ for a high-speed one. In the case of rubber-driven model aeroplanes the pitch ratio is often carried much higher, even to over 3.

Mr. T.W.K. Clarke recommends a pitch angle of 45°, or less, at the tips, and a pitch ratio of 3-1/7 (with an angle of 45°). Within limits the higher the pitch ratio the better the efficiency. The higher the pitch ratio the slower may be the rate of revolution. Now in a rubber motor we do not want the rubber to untwist (run out) too quickly; with too fine a pitch the propeller "races," or does something remarkably like it. It certainly revolves with an abnormally high percentage of slip. And for efficiency it is certainly desirable to push this ratio to its limit; but there is also the question of the

§ 9. **Diameter.**—"The diameter (says Mr. T. W.K. Clarke) should be equal to one-quarter the span of the machine."

If we increase the diameter we shall decrease the pitch ratio. From experiments which the writer has made he prefers a lower pitch ratio and increased diameter, viz. a pitch ratio of 1·5, and a diameter of one-third to even one-half the span, or even more.[27] Certainly not less than one-third. Some model makers indulge in a large pitch ratio, angle, diameter, and blade area as well, but such a course is not to be recommended.

§ 10. **Theoretical Pitch.**—Theoretically the pitch (from boss to tip) should at all points be the same; the boss or centre of the blade at right angles to the plane of rotation, and the angle decreasing as one approaches the tips. This is obvious when one considers that the whole blade has to move forward the same amount. In the diagrams Figs. 23 and 24 the tip A of the propeller travels a distance $= 2 \pi R$ every revolution. At a point D on the blade, distant r from the centre, the distance is $2 \pi r$. In both instances the two points must advance a distance equal to the pitch, i.e. the distance represented by P O.

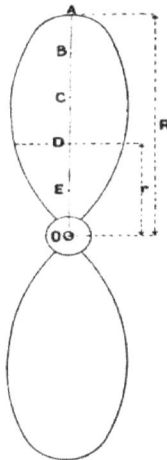

Fig. 23.

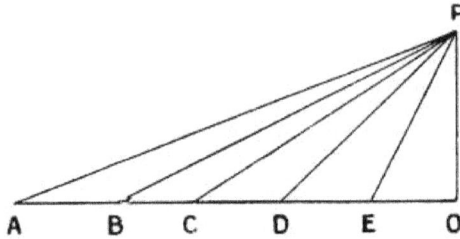

FIG. 24.

A O = 2ΠR; D O = 2ΠR.

A will move along A P, B along B P, and so on. The angles at the points A, B, C ... (Fig. 24), showing the angles at which the corresponding parts of the blade at A, B, C ... in Fig. 23 must be set in order that a uniform pitch may be obtained.

§ 11. If the pitch be not uniform then there will be some portions of the blade which will drag through the air instead of affording useful thrust, and others which will be doing more than they ought, putting air in motion which had better be left quiet. This uniform total pitch for all parts of the propeller is (as already stated) a decreasing rate of pitch from the centre to the edge. With a total pitch of 5 ft., and a radius of 4 ft., and an angle at the circumference of 6°, then the angle of pitch at a point midway between centre and circumference should be 12°, in order that the total pitch may be the same at all parts.

§ 12. **To Ascertain the Pitch of a Propeller.**—Take any point on one of the blades, and carefully measure the inclination of the blade at that point to the plane of rotation.

If the angle so formed be about 19° (19·45),[28] i.e., 1 in 3, and the point 5 in. from the centre, then every revolution this point will travel a distance

$$2 \pi r = 2 \times 22/7 \times 5 = 31 \cdot 34.$$

Now since the inclination is 1 in 3,[29] the propeller will travel forward theoretically one-third of this distance, or

$$31 \cdot 43/3 = 10 \cdot 48 = 10\tfrac{1}{2} \text{ in. approx.}$$

Similarly any other case may be dealt with. If the propeller have a uniform *constant angle* instead of a uniform pitch, then the pitch may be calculated at a point about one-third the length of the blade from the tip.

§ 13. **Hollow-Faced Blades.**[30]—It must always be carefully borne in mind that a propeller is nothing more nor less than a particular form of aeroplane specially designed to travel a helical path. It should, therefore, be hollow faced and partake of the "stream line" form, a condition not fulfilled if the face of the blade be flat—such a surface cutting into the air with considerable shock, and by no means creating as little undesirable motion in the surrounding medium as possible.

It must not be forgotten that a curved face blade has of necessity an increasing pitch from the cutting to the trailing edge (considering, of course, any particular section). In such a case the pitch is the *mean effective pitch*.

§ 14. **Blade Area.**—We have already referred to the fact that the function of a propeller is to produce dynamic thrust—to drive the aeroplane forward by driving the air backwards. At the same time it is most desirable for efficiency that the air should be set in motion as little as possible, this being so much power wasted; to obtain the greatest reaction or thrust the greatest possible volume of air should be accelerated to the smallest velocity.

In marine engineering in slow-speed propellers (where cavitation[31] does not come in) narrow blades are usually used. In high-speed marine propellers (where cavitation is liable to occur) the projected area of the blades is sometimes as much as 0·6 of the total disk area. In the case of aerial propellers, where cavitation does not occur, or not unless the velocity be a very high one (1500 or more a minute), narrow blades are the best. Experiments in marine propulsion also show that the thrust depends more on the disk area than on the width of the blades. All the facts tend to show that for efficiency the blades of the propeller should be narrow, in order that the air may not be acted on for too long a time, and so put too much in motion, and the blades be so separated that one blade does not disturb the molecules of air upon which the next following one must act. Both in the case of marine and aerial propellers multiplicity of blades (i.e. increased blade area) tends to inefficiency of action, apart altogether from the question of weight and constructional difficulties. The question of increasing pitch in the case of hollow-faced blades, considered in the last paragraph, has a very important bearing on the point we are considering. To make a wide blade under such circumstances would be to soon obtain an excessive angle.

In the case of a flat blade the same result holds, because the air has by the contact of its molecules with the "initial minimum width" been already accelerated up to its final velocity, and further area is not only wasted, but inimical to good flights, being our old bugbear "weight in excess."

Requisite strength and stiffness, of course, set a limit on the final narrowness of the blades, apart from other considerations.

§ 15. The velocity with which the propeller is rotated has also an important bearing on this point; but a higher speed than 900 r.p.m. does not appear desirable, and even 700 or less is generally preferable.[32] In case of twin-screw propellers, with an angle at the tips of 40° to 45°, as low a velocity of 500 or even less would be still better.[33]

§ 16. **Shrouding.**—No improvement whatever is obtained by the use of any kind of shrouding or ring round the propeller tips, or by corrugating the surface of the propeller, or by using cylindrical or cone-shaped propeller chamber or any kind of air guide either before or after the propeller; allow it to revolve in as free an air-feed as possible, the air does not fly off under centrifugal force, but is powerfully sucked inwards in a well-designed propeller.

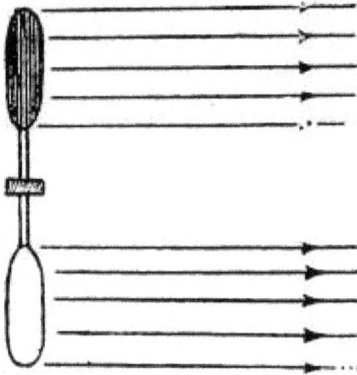

Fig. 25.
A Tube of Air.

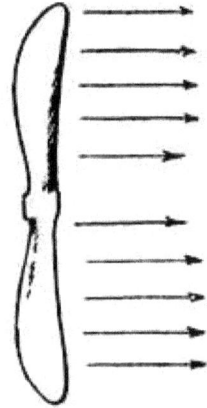

Fig. 26.
A Cylinder of Air.

§ 17. **General Design.**—The propeller should be so constructed as to act upon a tube and not a "cylinder" of air. Many flying toys (especially the French ones) are constructed with propellers of the cylinder type. Ease of manufacture and the contention that those portions of the blades adjacent to the boss do little work, and a slight saving in weight, are arguments that can be urged in their favour. But all the central cut away part offers resistance in the line of travel, instead of exerting its proportionate propulsive power, and their efficiency is affected by such a practice.

§ 18. A good **Shape** for the blades[34] is rectangular with rounded corners; the radius of the circle for rounding off the corners may be taken as about one-quarter of the width of the blade. The shape is not *truly rectangular, for the width of this rectangular at (near) the boss should be one-half the width at the tip.*

The thickness should diminish uniformly from the boss to the tip. (In models the thickness should be as little as is consistent with strength to keep down the weight). *The pitch uniform and large.*

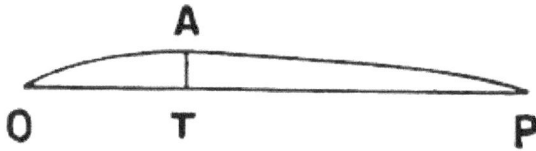

FIG. 27.—O T = 1/3 O P.

§ 19. **The Blades, two in number,** and hollow faced—the maximum concavity being one-third the distance from the entering to the trailing edge; the ratio of A T to O P (the width) being 0·048 or 1 : 21, these latter considerations being founded on the analogy between a propeller and the aerofoil surface. (If the thickness be varied from the entering to the trailing edge the greatest thickness should be towards the former.) The convex surface of the propeller must be taken into account, in fact, it is no less important than the concave, and the entire surface must be given a true "stream line" form.

Fig. 28.   **Fig. 29.**

If the entering and trailing edge be not both straight, but one be curved as in Fig. 28, then the straight edge must be made the *trailing* edge. And if both be curved as in Fig. 29, then the *concave* edge must be the trailing edge.

§ 19. **Propeller Design.**—To design a propeller, proceed as follows. Suppose the diameter 14 in. and the pitch three times the diameter, i.e. 52 in. (See Fig. 30.)

Take one-quarter scale, say. Draw a centre line A B of convenient length, set of half the pitch 52 in.— ¼ scale = 5¼ in. = C - D. Draw lines through C and D at right angles to C D.

With a radius equal to half the diameter (i.e. in this case 1¾ in.) of the propeller, describe a semicircle E B F and complete the parallelogram F H G E. Divide the semicircle into a number of equal parts; twelve is a convenient number to take, then each division subtends an angle of 15° at the centre D.

Divide one of the sides E G into the same number of equal parts (twelve) as shown. Through these points draw lines parallel to F E or H G.

And through the twelve points of division on the semicircle draw lines parallel to F H or E G as shown. The line drawn through the successive intersections of these lines is the path of the tip of the blade through half a revolution, viz. the line H S O T E.

S O T X gives the angle at the tip of the blades = 44°.

Let the shape of the blade be rectangular with rounded corners, and let the breadth at the tip be twice that at the boss.

Then the area (neglecting the rounded off corners) is 10½ sq. in.

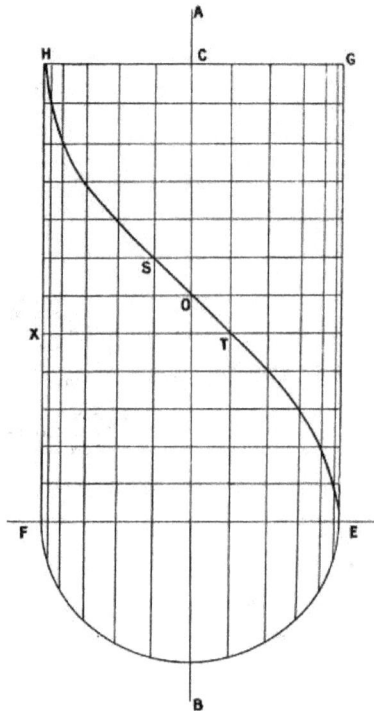

FIG. 30.—PROPELLER DESIGN.
ONE QUARTER SCALE. DIAMETER 14 IN. PITCH 52 IN. ANGLE AT TIP 44°.

The area being that of a rectangle 7 in. × 1 in. = 7 sq. in. plus area of two triangles, base ½ in., height 7 in. Now area of triangle = half base × height. Therefore area of both triangles = ½ in. × 7 in. = 3½ sq. in. Now the area of the disc swept out by the propeller is

$$\pi/4 \times (\text{diam.})^2 \ (\pi = 22/7)$$

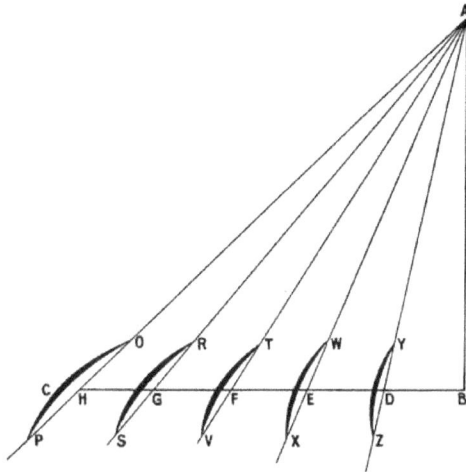

FIG. 31.—PROPELLER DESIGN.
SCALE ONE-EIGHTH FOR **A B** AND **B C**; BUT SECTIONS OF BLADE ARE
FULL-SIZED.

And if d A r = the "disc area ratio" we have

$$(d \text{ A } r) \times \pi/4 \times (14)^2 = \text{area of blade} = 10\frac{1}{2},$$

whence d A r = 0·07 about.

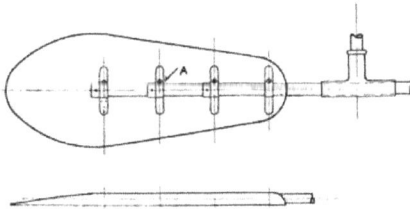
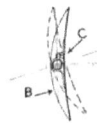

Fig. 32.   **Fig. 33.**

In Fig. 31 set off A B equal to the pitch of the propeller (42 in.), one-eighth
scale. Set off B C at right angles to A B and equal to

$\pi \times \text{diameter} = 22/7 \times 14 = 44$ in. to scale $5\frac{1}{2}$ in.

Divide B C into a convenient number of equal parts in the figure; five only
are taken, D, E, F, G, H; join A D, A E, A F, A G, A H and produce them;
mark off distances P O, S R, Y T ... equal to the width of the blade at these
points (H P = H O; G S = G R ...) and sketch in the sections of blade as
desired. In the figure the greatest concavity of the blade is supposed to be
one-third the distances P O, S R ... from PS.... The concavity is somewhat

exaggerated. The angles A H B, A G B, A F B ... represent the pitch angle at the points H, G, F ... of the blade.

Similarly any other design may be dealt with; in a propeller of 14 in. diameter the diameter of the "boss" should not be more than 10/16 in.

§ 20. **Experiments with Propellers.**—The propeller design shown in Figs. 32 and 33, due to Mr. G. de Havilland,[35] is one very suitable for experimental purposes. A single tube passing through a T-shaped boss forms the arms. On the back of the metal blade are riveted four metallic clips; these clips being tightened round the arm by countersunk screws in the face of the blade.

The tube and clips, etc., are all contained with the back covering of the blade, as shown in Fig. 35, if desired, the blade then practically resembling a wooden propeller. The construction, it will be noticed, allows of the blade being set at any angle, constant or otherwise; also the pitch can be constant or variable as desired, and any "shape" of propeller can be fitted.

The advantage of being able to *twist* the blade (within limits) on the axis is one not to be underestimated in experimental work.

Fig. 34.—The Author's Propeller Testing Apparatus.

With a view to ascertain some practical and reliable data with respect to the *dynamic*, or actual thrust given when moving through free air at the velocity of actual travel, the author experimented with the apparatus illustrated in Figs. 34 and 35, which is so simple and obvious as to require scarcely any explanation.

The wires were of steel, length not quite 150 ft., fitted with wire strainers for equalising tension, and absolutely free from "kinks." As shown most plainly in Fig. 35, there were two parallel wires sufficiently far apart for the action of one propeller not to affect the other. Calling these two wires A and B, and two propellers x and y, then x is first tried on A and y on B. Results carefully noted.

FIG. 35.—PROPELLER TESTING.
SHOWING DISTANCE SEPARATING THE TWO WIRES.

Then x is tried on B and y on A, and the results again carefully noted. If the results confirm one another, the power used in both cases being the same, well and good; if not, adjustments, etc., are made in the apparatus until satisfactory results are obtained. This was done when the propellers "raced" one against the other. At other times one wire only was made use of, and the time and distance traversed was noted in each case. Propellers were driven through smoke, and with silk threads tied to a light framework slightly larger than their disc area circumference. Results of great interest were arrived at. These results have been assumed in much that has been said in the foregoing paragraphs.

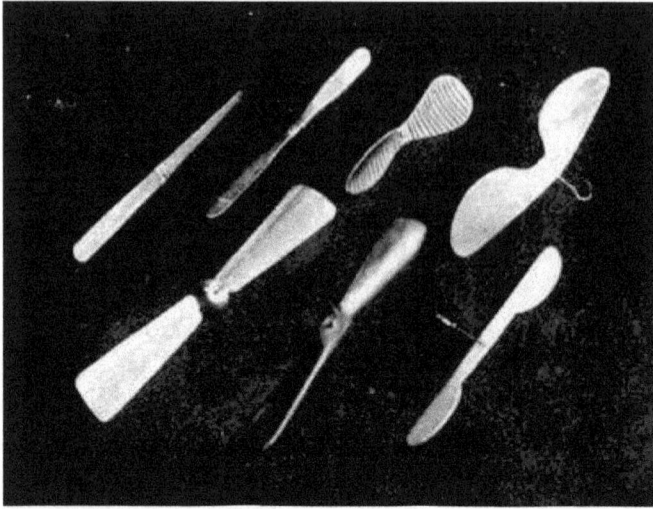

Fig. 36.—One Group of Propellers Tested by the Author.

Briefly put, these results showed:—

1. The inefficiency of a propeller of the fan blower or of the static thrust type.

2. The advantage of using propellers having hollow-faced blades and large diameter.

3. That diameter was more useful than blade area, i.e. given a certain quantity (weight) of wood, make a long thin blade and not a shorter one of more blade area—blade area, i.e., as proportionate to its corresponding disc area.

4. That the propeller surface should be of true stream-line form.

5. That it should act on a cylinder and not tubes of air.

6. That a correctly designed and proportioned propeller was just as efficacious in a small size of 9 in. to 28 in. as a full-sized propeller on a full-sized machine.

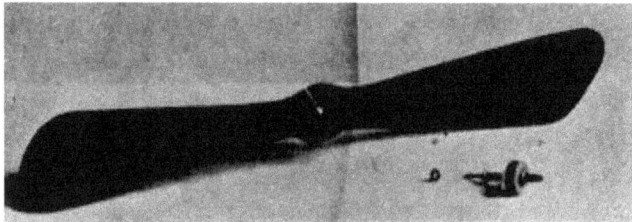

FIG. 37.—AN EFFICIENT PROPELLER, BUT RATHER HEAVY.
Ball bearings, old and new. Note difference in sizes and weights.
Propeller, 14 in. diam.; weight 36 grammes.

A propeller of the static-thrust type was, of course, "first off," sometimes 10 ft. or 12 ft. ahead, or even more; but the correctly designed propeller gradually gathered up speed and acceleration, just as the other fell off and lost it, and finally the "dynamic" finished along its corresponding wire far ahead of the "static," sometimes twice as far, sometimes six times. "Freak" propellers were simply not in it.

FIG. 38.—"VENNA" PROPELLER.
A 20 PER CENT. MORE EFFICIENT PROPELLER THAN THAT SHOWN IN FIG. 41; 14 PER CENT. LIGHTER; 6 PER CENT. BETTER IN DYNAMIC THRUST—14 IN. DIAM.; WEIGHT 31 GRAMMES.

Metal propellers of constant angle, as well as wooden ones of uniform (constant) pitch, were tested; the former gave good results, but not so good as the latter.

The best angle of pitch (at the tip) was found to be from 20° to 30°.

In all cases when the slip was as low as 25 per cent., or even somewhat less, nearly 20 per cent., a distinct "back current" of air was given out by the screw. This "slip stream," as it is caused, is absolutely necessary for efficiency.

§ 21. Fabric-covered screws did not give very efficient results; the only point in their use on model aeroplanes is their extreme lightness. Two such propellers of 6 in. diameter can be made to weigh less than 1/5 oz. the pair; but wooden propellers (built-up principle) have been made 5 in. diameter and 1/12 oz. in weight.

§ 22. Further experiments were made with twin screws mounted on model aeroplanes. In one case two propellers, both turning in the *same* direction, were mounted (without any compensatory adjustment for torque) on a model, total weight 1½ lb. Diameter of each propeller 14 in.; angle of blade at tip 25°. The result was several good flights—the model (*see* Fig. 49c) was slightly unsteady across the wind, that was all.

In another experiment two propellers of same diameter, pitch, etc., but of shape similar to those shown in Figs. 28 and 29, were tried as twin propellers on the same machine. The rubber motors were of equal weight and strength.

The model described circled to the right or left according to the position of the curved-shaped propeller, whether on the left or right hand, thereby showing its superiority in dynamic thrust. Various alterations were made, but always with the same result. These experiments have since been confirmed, and there seems no doubt that the double-curved shaped blade *is* superior. (See Fig. 39.)

§ 23. **The Fleming-Williams Propeller.**—A chapter on propellers would scarcely be complete without a reference to the propeller used on a machine claiming a record of over a quarter of a mile. This form of propeller, shown in the group in Fig. 36 (top right hand), was found by the writer to be extremely deficient in dynamic thrust, giving the worst result of any shown there.

FIG. 39.—CURVED DOUBLE PROPELLER.
THE MOST EFFICIENT TYPE YET TESTED BY THE WRITER, WHEN THE BLADE IS MADE HOLLOW-FACED. WHEN GIVEN TO THE WRITER TO TEST IT WAS FLAT-FACED ON ONE SIDE.

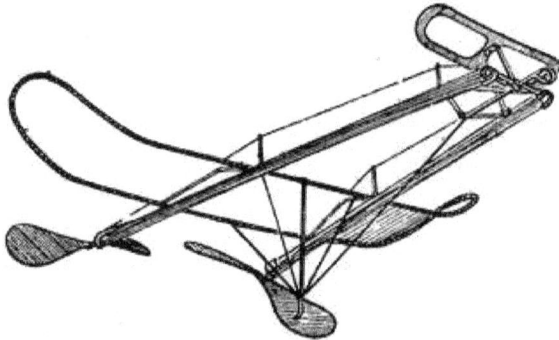

Fig. 40.—The Fleming-Williams Model.

It possesses large blade area, large pitch angle—more than 45° at the tip— and large diameter. These do not combine to propeller efficiency or to efficient dynamic thrust; but they do, of course, combine to give the propeller a very slow rotational velocity. Provided they give *sufficient* thrust to cause the model to move through the air at a velocity capable of sustaining it, a long flight may result, not really owing to true efficiency on the part of the propellers,[36] but owing to the check placed on their revolutions per minute by their abnormal pitch angle, etc. The amount of rubber used is very great for a 10 oz. model, namely, 34 strands of 1/16 in. square rubber to each propeller, i.e. 68 strands in all.

FIG. 41.—THE SAME IN FLIGHT.
(REPRODUCED BY PERMISSION FROM "THE AERO.")

On the score of efficiency, when it is desired to make a limited number of turns give the longest flight (which is the problem one always has to face when using a rubber motor) it is better to make use of an abnormal diameter, say, more than half the span, and using a tip pitch angle of 25°, than to make use of an abnormal tip pitch 45° and more, and large blade area. In a large pitch angle so much energy is wasted, not in dynamic thrust, but in transverse upsetting torque. On no propeller out of dozens and dozens that I have tested have I ever found a tip-pitch of more than 35° give a good dynamic thrust; and for length of flight velocity due to dynamic thrust must be given due weight, as well as the duration of running down of the rubber motor.

§ 24. Of built up or carved out and twisted wooden propellers, the former give the better result; the latter have an advantage, however, in sometimes weighing less.

CHAPTER VI.

THE QUESTION OF SUSTENTATION
THE CENTRE OF PRESSURE.

§ 1. Passing on now to the study of an aeroplane actually in the air, there are two forces acting on it, the upward lift due to the air (i.e. to the movement of the aeroplane supposed to be continually advancing on to fresh, undisturbed *virgin* air), and the force due to the weight acting vertically downwards. We can consider the resultant of all the upward sustaining forces as acting at a single point—that point is called the "Centre of Pressure."

Suppose A B a vertical section of a flat aerofoil, inclined at a small angle *a* to the horizon C, the point of application of the resultant upward 'lift,' D the point through which the weight acts vertically downwards. Omitting for the moment the action of propulsion, if these two forces balance there will be equilibrium; but to do this they must pass through the same point, but as the angle of inclination varies, so does the centre of pressure, and some means must be employed whereby if C and D coincide at a certain angle the aeroplane will come back to the correct angle of balance if the latter be altered.

In a model the means must be automatic. Automatic stability depends for its action upon the movement of the centre of pressure when the angle of incidence varies. When the angle of incidence increases the centre of pressure moves backwards towards the rear of the aerofoil, and vice versa.

Let us take the case when steady flight is in progress and C and D are coincident, suppose the velocity of the wind suddenly to increase—increased lifting effect is at once the result, and the fore part of the machine rises, i.e. the angle of incidence increases and the centre of pressure moves back to some point in the rear of C D. The weight is now clearly trying to pull the nose of the aeroplane down, and the "lift" tending to raise the tail. The result being an alteration of the angle of incidence, or angle of attack as it is called, until it resumes its original position of equilibrium. A drop in the wind causes exactly an opposite effect.

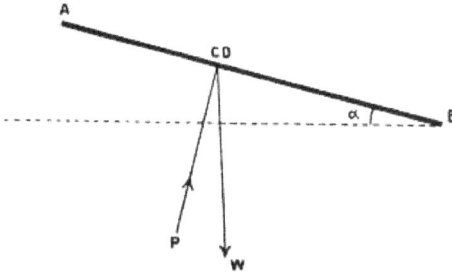

Fig. 42.

§ 2. The danger lies in "oscillations" being set up in the line of flight due to changes in the position of the centre of pressure. Hence the device of an elevator or horizontal tail for the purpose of damping out such oscillations.

§ 3. But the aerofoil surface is not flat, owing to the increased "lift" given by arched surfaces, and a much more complicated set of phenomena then takes place, the centre of pressure moving forward until a certain critical angle of incidence is reached, and after this a reversal takes place, the centre of pressure then actually moving backwards.

The problem then consists in ascertaining the most efficient aerocurve to give the greatest "lift" with the least "drift," and, having found it, to investigate again experimentally the movements of the centre of pressure at varying angles, and especially to determine at what angle (about) this "reversal" takes place.

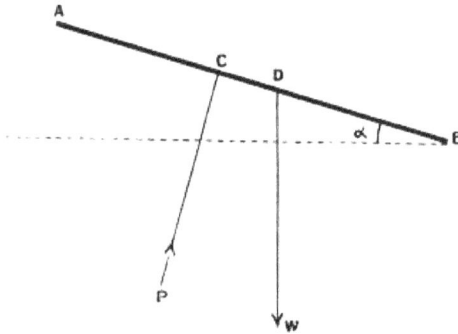

Fig. 43.

§ 4. Natural automatic stability (the only one possible so far as models are concerned) necessitates permanent or a permanently recurring coincidence (to coin a phrase) of the centre of gravity and the centre of pressure: the former is, of course, totally unaffected by the vagaries of the latter, any shifting of which produces a couple tending to destroy equilibrium.

§ 5. As to the best form of camber (for full sized machine) possibly more is known on this point than on any other in the whole of aeronautics.

In Figs. 44 and 45 are given two very efficient forms of cambered surfaces for models.

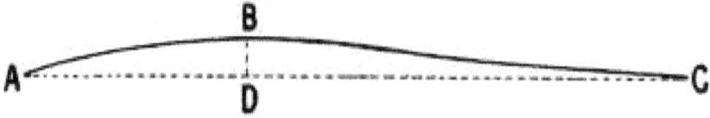

FIG. 44.—AN EFFICIENT FORM OF CAMBER.
B D MAXIMUM ALTITUDE. A C CHORD. RATIO OF B D: A C :: 1:17. A D 1/3 OF A C.

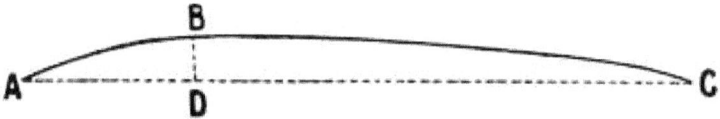

FIG. 45.—ANOTHER EFFICIENT FORM.
RATIO OF B D TO A C 1 TO 17. AD RATHER MORE THAN ¼ OF A C.

The next question, after having decided the question of aerocurve, or curvature of the planes, is at what angle to set the cambered surface to the line of flight. This brings us to the question of the—

§ 6. **Dipping Front Edge.**—The leading or front edge is not tangential to the line of flight, but to a relative upward wind. It is what is known as the "cyclic up-current," which exists in the neighbourhood of the entering edge. Now, as we have stated before, it is of paramount importance that the aerofoil should receive the air with as little shock as possible, and since this up-current does really exist to do this, it must travel through the air with a dipping front edge. The "relative wind" (the only one with which we are concerned) *is* thereby met tangentially, and as it moves onward through the air the cambered surface (or aerocurve) gradually transforms this upward trend into a downward wake, and since by Newton's law, "Action and reaction are equal and opposite," we have an equal and opposite upward reaction.

We now know that the top (or convex side) of the cambered surface is practically almost as important as the underneath or concave side in bringing this result about.

The exact amount of "dipping edge," and the exact angle at which the chord of the aerocurve, or cambered surface, should be set to the line of flight— whether at a positive angle, at no angle, or at a negative angle—is one best determined by experiment on the model in question.

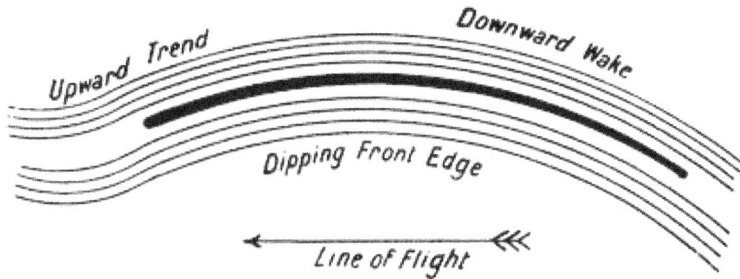

Fig. 46.

But *if at any angle, that angle either way should be a very small one.* If you wish to be very scientific you can give the underside of the front edge a negative angle of 5° to 7° for about one-eighth of the total length of the section, after that a positive angle, gradually increasing until you finally finish up at the trailing edge with one of 4°. Also, the form of cambered surface should be a paraboloid—not arc or arc of circles. The writer does not recommend such an angle, but prefers an attitude similar to that adopted in the Wright machine, as in Fig. 47.

§ 7. Apart from the attitude of the aerocurve: *the greatest depth of the camber should be at one-third of the length of the section from the front edge, and the total depth measured from the top surface to the chord at this point should not be more than one-seventeenth of the length of section.*

§ 8. It is the greatest mistake in model aeroplanes to make the camber otherwise than very slight (in the case of surfaced aerofoils the resistance is much increased), and aerofoils with anything but a *very slight* arch are liable to be very unstable, for the aerocurve has always a decided tendency to "follow its own curve."

Fig. 47.—Attitude of Wright Machine.

The nature of the aerocurve, its area, the angle of inclination of its chord to the line of flight, its altitude, etc., are not the only important matters one must consider in the case of the aerofoil, we must also consider—

§ 9. Its **Aspect Ratio**, i.e. the ratio of the span (length) of the aerofoil to the chord—usually expressed by span/chord. In the Farman machine this ratio is 5·4; Blériot, 4·3; Short, 6 to 7·5; Roe triplane, 7·5; a Clark flyer, 9·6.

Now the higher the aspect ratio the greater should be the efficiency. Air escaping by the sides represents loss, and the length of the sides should be kept short. A broader aerofoil means a steeper angle of inclination, less stability, unnecessary waste of power, and is totally unsuited for a model— to say nothing of a full-sized machine.

In models this aspect ratio may with advantage be given a higher value than in full-sized machines, where it is well known a practical safe constructional limit is reached long before theory suggests the limit. The difficulty consists in constructing models having a very high aspect ratio, and yet possessing sufficient strength and lightness for successful flight. It is in such a case as this where the skill and ingenuity of the designer and builder come in.

It is this very question of aspect ratio which has given us the monoplane, the biplane, and the triplane. A biplane has a higher aspect ratio than a monoplane, and a triplane (see above) a higher ratio still.

It will be noticed the Clark model given has a considerably higher aspect ratio, viz. 9·6. And even this can be exceeded.

An aspect ratio of 10:1 *or even* 12:1 *should be used if possible.*[37]

§ 10. **Constant or Varying Camber.**—Some model makers vary the camber of their aerofoils, making them almost flat in some parts, with considerable camber in others; the tendency in some cases being to flatten the central portions of the aerofoil, and with increasing camber towards the tips. In others the opposite is done. The writer has made a number of experiments on this subject, but cannot say he has arrived at any very decisive results, save that the camber should in all cases be (as stated before) very slight, and so far as his experiments do show anything, they incline towards the further flattening of the camber in the end portions of the aerofoil. It must not be forgotten that a flat-surfaced aerofoil, constructed as it is of more or less elastic materials, assumes a natural camber, more or less, when driven horizontally through the air. Reference has been made to a reversal of the—

§ 11. **Centre of Pressure on Arched Surfaces.**—Wilbur Wright in his explanation of this reversal says: "This phenomenon is due to the fact that at small angles the wind strikes the forward part of the aerofoil surface on the upper side instead of the lower, and thus this part altogether ceases to lift, instead of being the most effective part of all." The whole question hangs on the value of the critical angle at which this reversal takes place; some experiments made by Mr. M.B. Sellers in 1906 (published in "Flight," May 14, 1910) place this angle between 16° and 20°. This angle is much above that used in model aeroplanes, as well as in actual full-sized machines. But the equilibrium of the model might be upset, not by a change of attitude on its part, but on that of the wind, or both combined. By giving (as already advised) the aerofoil a high aspect ratio we limit the travel of the centre of pressure, for a high aspect ratio means, as we have seen, a short chord; and this is an additional reason for making the aspect ratio as high as practically possible. The question is, is the critical angle really as high as Mr. Seller's experiments would show. Further experiments are much needed.

CHAPTER VII.

MATERIALS FOR AEROPLANE
CONSTRUCTION.

§ 1. The choice of materials for model aeroplane construction is more or less limited, if the best results are to be obtained. The lightness absolutely essential to success necessitates—in addition to skilful building and best disposition of the materials—materials of no undue weight relative to their strength, of great elasticity, and especially of great resilience (capacity to absorb shock without injury).

§ 2. **Bamboo.**—Bamboo has per pound weight a greater resilience than any other suitable substance (silk and rubber are obviously useless as parts of the *framework* of an aeroplane). On full-sized machines the difficulty of making sufficiently strong connections and a liability to split, in the larger sizes, are sufficient reasons for its not being made more use of; but it makes an almost ideal material for model construction. The best part to use (split out from the centrepiece) is the strip of tough wood immediately below the hard glazed surface. For struts, spars, and ribs it can be used in this manner, and for the long strut supporting the rubber motor an entire tube piece should be used of the requisite strength required; for an ordinary rubber motor (one yard long), 30 to 50 strands, this should be a piece 3/8 in. in diameter, and weight about 5/8 oz. per ft. *Bamboo may be bent* by either the "dry" heat from a spirit lamp or stove, or it may be steamed, the latter for preference, as there is no danger of "scorching" the fibres on the inside of the bend. When bent (as in the case of other woods) it should be bound on to a "former" having a somewhat greater curvature than the curve required, because when cool and dry it will be sure to "go back" slightly. It must be left on the former till quite dry. When bending the "tube" entire, and not split portions thereof, it should be immersed in very hot, or even boiling, water for some time before steaming. The really successful bending of the tube *en bloc* requires considerable patience and care.

Bamboo is inclined to split at the ends, and some care is required in making "joints." The ribs can be attached to the spars by lashing them to thin T strips of light metal, such as aluminium. Thin thread, or silk, is preferable to very thin wire for lashing purpose, as the latter "gives" too much, and cuts into the fibres of the wood as well.

§ 3. **Ash**, **Spruce**, **Whitewood** are woods that are also much used by model makers. Many prefer the last named owing to its uniform freedom from knots and ease with which it can be worked. It is stated 15 per cent. additional strength can be imparted by using hot size and allowing it to soak into the wood at an increase only of 3·7 per cent. of weight. It is less than half the weight of bamboo, but has a transverse rupture of only 7,900 lb. per sq. in. compared to 22,500 in the case of bamboo tubing (thickness one-eighth diameter) and a resilience per lb. weight of slightly more than one half. Some model makers advocate the use of **poplar** owing to its extreme lightness (about the same as whitewood), but its strength is less in the ratio of about 4:3; its resilience is very slightly more. It must be remembered that wood of the same kind can differ much as to its strength, etc., owing to what part of the tree it may have been cut from, the manner in which it may have been seasoned, etc. For model aeroplanes all wood used should have been at least a year in seasoning, and should be so treated when in the structure that it cannot absorb moisture.

If we take the resilience of ash as 1, then (according to Haswell) relative resilience of beech is 0·86, and spruce 0·64.

The strongest of woods has a weight when well seasoned of about 40 lb. per cub. ft. and a tenacity of about 10,000 lb. per sq. in.

FIG. 47A.—"AEROPLANE ALMA."
A VERY EFFECTIVE FRENCH TOY MONOPLANE.

§ 4. **Steel.**—Ash has a transverse rupture of 14,300 lb. per sq. in., steel tubing (thickness = 1/30 its diameter) 100,000 lb. per sq. in. Ash weighs per cub. ft. 47 lb., steel 490. Steel being more than ten times as heavy as ash—but a transverse rupture stress seven times as high.

Bamboo in tube form, thickness one-third of diameter, has a transverse rupture of 22,500 lb. per sq. in., and a weight of 55 lb. per cub. ft.

Steel then is nine times as heavy as bamboo—and has a transverse rupture stress 4·4 times as great. In comparing these three substances it must be carefully borne in mind that lightness and strength are not the only things that have to be provided for in model aeroplane building; there is the question of *resistance*—we must offer as small a cross-section to moving through the air as possible.

Now while ash or bamboo and certain other timbers may carry a higher load per unit of weight than steel, they will present about three to three and a half times the cross-section, and this produces a serious obstacle, while otherwise meeting certain requirements that are most desirable. Steel tubing of sufficiently small bore is not, so far as the writer knows, yet on the market in England. In France very thin steel tubes are made of round, oval, hexagon, etc., shape, and of accurate thickness throughout, the price being about 18s. a lb.

Although suitable steel tubing is not yet procurable under ordinary circumstances, umbrella steel is.

§ 5. **Umbrella Section Steel** is a section 5/32 in. by 1/8 in. deep, 6 ft. long weighing 2·1 oz., and a section 3/32 in. across the base by 1/8 in. deep, 6 ft. long weighing 1·95 oz.

It is often stated that umbrella ribs are too heavy—but this entirely depends on the length you make use of, in lengths of 25 in. for small aerofoils made from such lengths it is so; but in lengths of 48 in. (two such lengths joined together) the writer has used it with great success; often making use of it now in his larger models; the particular size used by him weighs 13½ grammes, to a length of 25 in. He has never had one of these aerofoils break or become kinked—thin piano wire is used to stay them and also for spars when employed—the front and ends of the aerofoil are of umbrella steel, the trailing edge of steel wire, comparatively thin, kept taut by steel wire stays.

§ 6. **Steel Wire.**—Tensile strength about 300,000 lb. per sq. in. For the aerofoil framework of small models and for all purposes of staying, or where a very strong and light tension is required, this substance is invaluable. Also for framework of light fabric covered propellers as well as for skids and shock absorber—also for hooks to hold the rubber motor strands, etc. No model is complete without it in some form or another.

§ 7. **Silk.**—This again is a *sine qua non*. Silk is the strongest of all organic substances for certain parts of aeroplane construction. It has, in its best form, a specific gravity of 1·3, and is three times as strong as linen, and twice as strong in the thread as hemp. Its finest fibres have a section of from 0·0010 to 0·0015 in diameter. It will sustain about 35,000 lb. per sq. in. of its cross section; and its suspended fibre should carry about 150,000 ft. of its own material. This is six times the same figure for aluminium, and equals about 75,000 lb. steel tenacity, and 50 more than is obtained with steel in the form of watch springs or wire. For aerofoil surface no substance can compare with it. But it must be used in the form of an "oiled" or specially treated silk.

Several such are on the market. Hart's "fabric" and "radium" silk are perhaps the best known. Silk weighs 62 lb. per cub. ft., steel has, we have seen, 490 lb., thus paying due regard to this and to its very high tensile strength it is superior to even steel wire stays.

§ 8. **Aluminium and Magnalium.**—Two substances about which a great deal has been heard in connection with model aeroplaning; but the writer does not recommend their use save in the case of fittings for scale models, not actual flyers, unless especially light ones meant to fly with the wind. Neither can compare with steel. Steel, it is true, is three times as heavy as aluminium, but it has four or five times its strength; and whereas aluminium and magnalium may with safety be given a permissible breaking strength of 60 per cent. and 80 per cent. respectively, steel can easily be given 80 per cent. Being also less in section, resistance to air travel is again less as in the case of wood. In fact, steel scores all round. Weight of magnalium : weight of aluminium :: 8:9.

§ 9. **Alloys.**—During recent years scores, hundreds, possibly thousands of different alloys have been tried and experimented on, but steel still easily holds its own. It is no use a substance being lighter than another volume for volume, it must be *lighter and stronger weight for weight*, to be superior for aeronautical purpose, and if the difference be but slight, question of *bulk* may decide it as offering *less resistance.*

§ 10. **Sheet Ebonite.**—This substance is sometimes useful for experiments with small propellers, for it can be bent and moulded in hot water, and when cold sets and keeps its shape. *Vulcanized fibre* can be used for same purpose. *Sheet celluloid* can be used in the same way, but in time it becomes brittle and shrinks. *Mica* should be avoided. *Jointless cane* in various sizes is a very useful material—the main aerofoil can be built of it, and it is useful for skids, and might be made more use of than it is.[38] *Three ply wood*, from 1/50 in. in thickness, is now on the market. Four or five ply wood can also be obtained. To those desiring to build models having wooden aerofoils such woods offer the advantage of great strength and extreme lightness.

Referring to Table V. (Timber) at the end of the book, apparently the most suitable wood is Lombardy poplar; but its light weight means increased bulk, i.e. additional air resistance. Honduras mahogany is really a better all-round wood, and beech is not far behind.

Resilience is an important factor. Ash heads the list; but mahogany's factor is also good, and in other respects superior.

Lombardy poplar ought to be a very good wood for propellers, owing to its lightness and the ease with which it can be worked.

Hollow reeds, and even *porcupine quills*, have been pressed into the service of the model maker, and owing to their great strength and extreme lightness, more especially the latter, are not without their uses.

CHAPTER VIII.

HINTS ON THE BUILDING OF MODEL AEROPLANES.

§ 1. The chief difficulty in the designing and building of model aeroplanes is to successfully combat the conflicting interests contained therein. Weight gives stability, but requires extra supporting surface or a higher speed, i.e. more power, i.e. more weight. Inefficiency in one part has a terrible manner of repeating itself; for instance, suppose the aerofoil surface inefficient—badly designed—this means more resistance; more resistance means more power, i.e. weight, i.e. more surface, and so on *ad infinitum.*

It is because of circumstances like the above that it is so difficult to *design* really good and efficient flying models; the actual building of them is not so difficult, but few tools are required, none that are expensive or difficult to use.

In the making of any particular model there are special points that require special attention; but there are certain general rules and features which if not adhered to and carefully carried out, or as carefully avoided, will cause endless trouble and failure.

§ 2. In constructing a model aeroplane, or, indeed, any piece of aerial apparatus, it is very important not to interrupt the continuity of any rib, tube, spar, etc., by drilling holes or making too thinned down holding places; if such be done, additional strength by binding (with thread, not wire), or by slipping a small piece of slightly larger tube over the other, must be imparted to the apparatus.

§ 3. Begin by making a simple monoplane, and afterwards as you gain skill and experience proceed to construct more elaborate and scientific models.

§ 4. Learn to solder—if you do not know how to—it is absolutely essential.

§ 5. Do not construct models (intended for actual flight) with a tractor screw-main plane in front and tail (behind). Avoid them as you would the plague. Allusion has already been made in the Introduction to the difficulty of getting the centre of gravity sufficiently forward in the case of Blériot models; again with the main aerofoil in front, it is this aerofoil and not the balancing elevator, or tail, that *first* encounters the upsetting gust, and the effect of such a gust acting first on the larger surface is often more than the balancer can rectify in time to avert disaster. The proper place for the propeller is behind, in the wake of the machine. If the screw be in front the backwash from it strikes the machine and has a decidedly retarding action. It is often contended that it drives the air at an increased velocity under (and over) the main aerofoil, and so gives a greater lifting effect. But for proper lifting effect which it can turn without effort into air columns of proper stream line form what the aerofoil requires is undisturbed air—not propeller backwash.

The rear of the model is the proper place for the propeller, in the centre of greatest air disturbance; in such a position it will recover a portion of the energy lost in imparting a forward movement to the air, caused by the resistance, the model generally running in such air—the slip of the screw is reduced to a corresponding degree—may even vanish altogether, and what is known as negative slip occur.

§ 6. Wooden or metal aerofoils are more efficient than fabric covered ones. But they are only satisfactory in the smaller sizes, owing, for one thing, to the smash with which they come to the ground. This being due to the high speed necessary to sustain their weight. For larger-sized models fabric covered aerofoils should be used.

§ 7. As to the shape of such, only three need be considered—the (*a*) rectangular, (*b*) the elongated ellipse, (*c*) the chamfered rear edge.

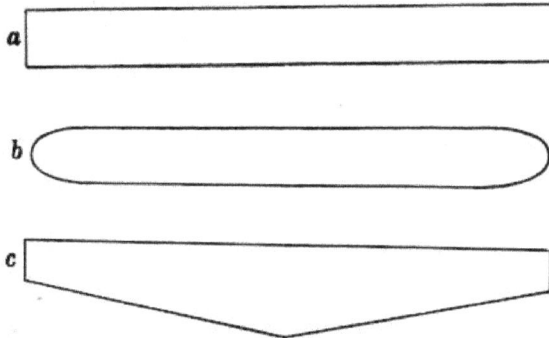

FIG. 48.—(A), (B), (C).

§ 8. The stretching of the fabric on the aerofoil framework requires considerable care, especially when using silk. It is quite possible, even in models of 3 ft. to 4 ft. spread, to do without "ribs," and still obtain a fairly correct aerocurve, if the material be stretched on in a certain way. It consists in getting a correct longitudinal and transverse tension. We will illustrate it by a simple case. Take a piece of thickish steel pianoforte wire, say, 18 in. long, bend it round into a circle, allowing ½ in. to 1 in. to overlap, tin and solder, bind this with soft very thin iron wire, and again solder (always use as little solder as possible). Now stitch on to this a piece of nainsook or silk, deforming the circle as you do so until it has the accompanying elliptical shape. The result is one of double curvature; the transverse curve (dihedral angle) can be regulated by cross threads or wires going from A to B and C to D.

Fig. 49.

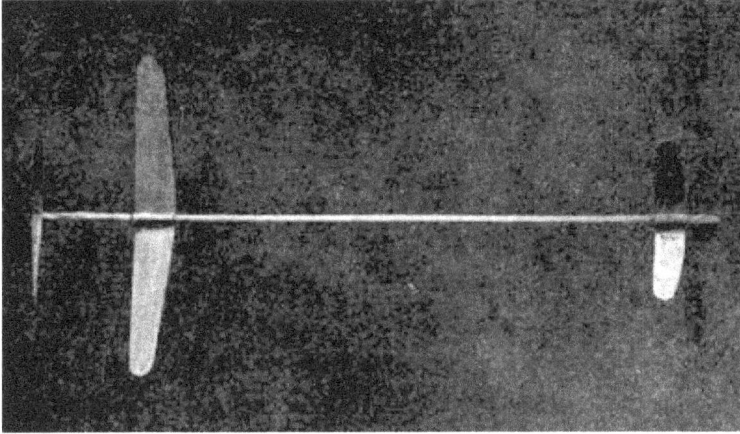
Fig. 49a.—Mr. T.W.K. Clarke's 1 oz. Model.

The longitudinal curve on the camber can be regulated by the original tension given to it, and by the manner of its fixing to the main framework. Suitable wire projections or loops should be bound to it by wire, and these fastened to the main framework by binding with *thin* rubber cord, a very useful method of fastening, since it acts as an excellent shock absorber, and "gives" when required, and yet possesses quite sufficient practical rigidity.

§ 9. Flexible joints are an advantage in a biplane; these can be made by fixing wire hooks and eyes to the ends of the "struts," and holding them in position by binding with silk or thread. Rigidity is obtained by use of steel wire stays or thin silk cord.

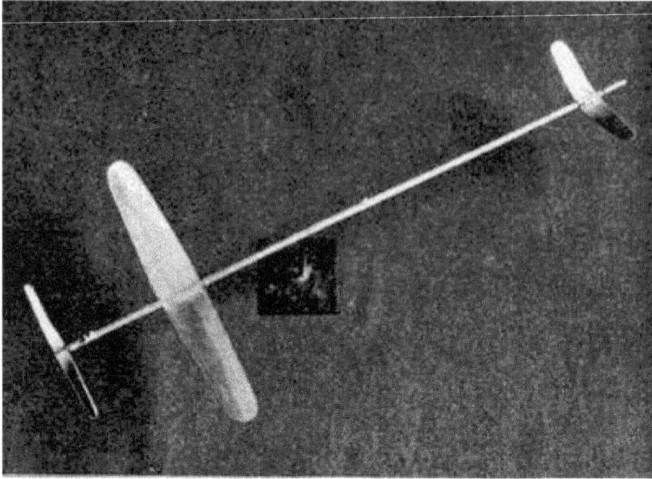

FIG. 49B.—MR. T.W.K. CLARKE'S 1 OZ. MODEL.
SHOWING THE POSITION OF C. OF G., OR POINT OF SUPPORT.

§ 10. Owing to the extra weight and difficulties of construction on so small a scale it is not desirable to use "double surface" aerofoils except on large size power-driven models.

§ 11. It is a good plan not to have the rod or tube carrying the rubber motor connected with the outrigger carrying the elevator, because the torque of the rubber tends to twist the carrying framework, and interferes with the proper and correct action of the elevator. If it be so connected the rod must be stayed with piano wire, both longitudinally (to overcome the pull which we know is very great), and also laterally, to overcome the torque.

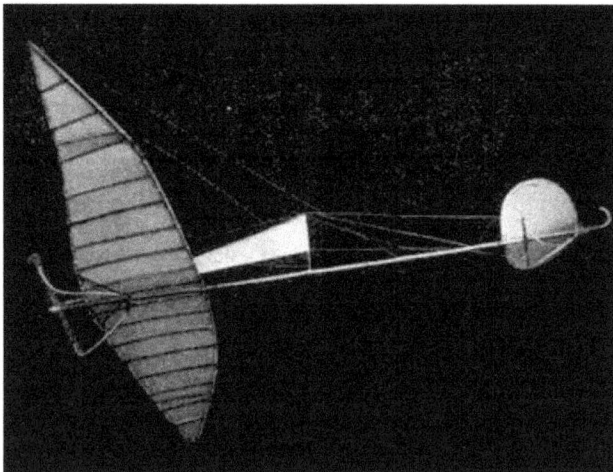

Fig. 49c.—A Large Model Aeroplane.
Shown without rubber or propellers. Designed and constructed by

the writer. As a test it was fitted with two 14 in. propellers revolving in the same direction, and made some excellent flights under these conditions, rolling slightly across the wind, but otherwise keeping quite steady. Total weight, 1½ lb.; length, 6 ft.; span of main aerofoil, 5 ft. Constructed of bamboo, cane, and steel wire. Front skids steel wire. Back skids cane. Aerofoil covering nainsook.

§ 12. Some builders place the rubber motor above the rod, or bow frame carrying the aerofoils, etc., the idea being that the pull of the rubber distorts the frame in such a manner as to "lift" the elevator, and so cause the machine to rise rapidly in the air. This it does; but the model naturally drops badly at the finish and spoils the effect. It is not a principle that should be copied.

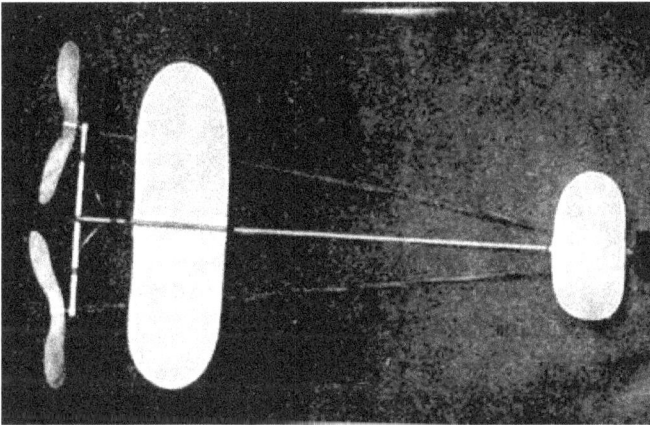

Fig. 49d.—A very Light Weight Model.
Constructed by the author. Provided with twin propellers of a modified Fleming-Williams type. This machine flew well when provided with an abnormal amount of rubber, owing to the poor dynamic thrust given by the propellers.

§ 13. In the Clarke models with the small front plane, the centre of pressure is slightly in front of the main plane.

The balancing point of most models is generally slightly in front, or just within the front edge of the main aerofoil. The best plan is to adjust the rod carrying the rubber motor and propeller until the best balance is obtained, then hang up the machine to ascertain the centre of gravity, and you will have (approximately) the centre of pressure.

FIG. 49E.—USEFUL FITTINGS FOR MODELS.
1. RUBBER TYRED WHEELS. 2. BALL-BEARING STEEL AXLE SHAFTS. 3.
BRASS WIRE STRAINERS WITH STEEL SCREWS; BREAKING STRAIN 200
LB. 4. MAGNALIUM TUBING. 5. STEEL EYEBOLT. 6. ALUMINIUM "T"
JOINT. 7. ALUMINIUM "L" PIECE. 8. BRASS BRAZED FITTINGS. 9.
BALL-BEARING THRUST. 10. FLAT ALUMINIUM "L" PIECE.
[*THE ABOVE ILLUSTRATIONS TAKEN (BY PERMISSION) FROM
MESSRS. GAMAGE'S CATALOGUE ON MODEL AVIATION*]

§ 14. The elevator (or tail) should be of the non-lifting type—in other words, the entire weight should be carried by the main aerofoil or aerofoils; the elevator being used simply as a balancer.[39] If the machine be so constructed that part of the weight be carried by the elevator, then either it must be large (in proportion) or set up at a large angle to carry it. Both mean considerably more resistance—which is to be avoided. In practice this means the propeller being some little distance in rear of the main supporting surface.

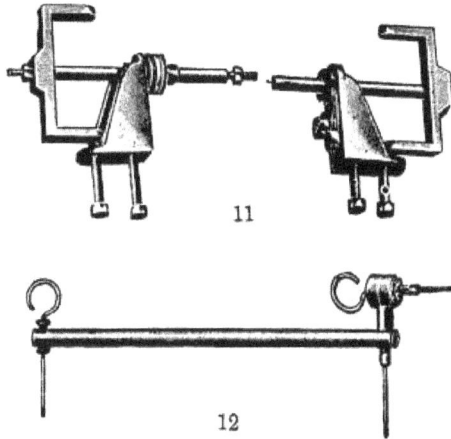

FIG. 49F.—USEFUL FITTINGS FOR MODELS.
11. ALUMINIUM BALL THRUST AND RACKET. 12. BALL-BEARING
PROPELLER, THRUST, AND STAY.
[*THE ABOVE ILLUSTRATIONS TAKEN (BY PERMISSION) FROM*
MESSRS. GAMAGE'S CATALOGUE ON MODEL AVIATION.]

§ 15. In actual flying models "skids" should be used and not "wheels"; the latter to be of any real use must be of large diameter, and the weight is prohibitive. Skids can be constructed of cane, imitation whalebone, steel watch or clock-spring, steel pianoforte wire. Steel mainsprings are better than imitation whalebone, but steel pianoforte wire best of all. For larger sized models bamboo is also suitable, as also ash or strong cane.

§ 16. Apart from or in conjunction with skids we have what are termed "shock absorbers" to lessen the shock on landing—the same substances can be used—steel wire in the form of a loop is very effectual; whalebone and steel springs have a knack of snapping. These shock absorbers should be so attached as to "give all ways" for a part side and part front landing as well as a direct front landing. For this purpose they should be lashed to the main frame by thin indiarubber cord.

§ 17. In the case of a biplane model the "gap" must not be less than the "chord"—preferably greater.

In a double monoplane (of the Langley type) there is considerable "interference," i.e. the rear plane is moving in air already acted on by the front one, and therefore moving in a downward direction. This means decreased efficiency. It can be overcome, more or less, by varying the dihedral angle at which the two planes are set; but cannot be got rid of altogether, or by placing them far apart. In biplanes not possessing a dihedral angle—the propeller can be placed *slightly* to one side—in order to neutralise the torque of the propeller—the best portion should be found by experiment—unless the pitch be very large; with a well designed propeller this is not by any means essential. If the propeller revolve clockwise, place it towards the right hand of the machine, and vice versa.

§ 18. In designing a model to fly the longest possible distance the monoplane type should be chosen, and when desiring to build one that shall remain the longest time in the air the biplane or triplane type should be adopted.[40] For the longest possible flight twin propellers revolving in opposite directions[41] are essential. To take a concrete case—one of the writer's models weighed complete with a single propeller 8½ oz. It was then altered and fitted with two propellers (same diameter and weight); this complete with double rubber weighed 10¼ oz. The advantage double the power. Weight increased only 20 per cent., resistance about 10 per cent., total 30 per cent. Gain 70 per cent. Or if the method of gearing advocated (see Geared Motors) be adopted then we shall have four bunches of rubber instead of two, and can thereby obtain so many more turns.[42] The length of the strands should be such as to render possible at least a thousand turns.

The propellers should be of large diameter and pitch (not less than 35° at the tips), of curved shape, as advocated in § 22 ch. v.; the aerofoil surface of as high an aspect ratio as possible, and but slight camber if any; this is a very difficult question, the question of camber, and the writer feels bound to admit he has obtained as long flights with surfaces practically flat, but which do, of course, camber slightly in a suitable wind, as with stiffer cambered surfaces.

Wind cambered surfaces are, however, totally unsuitable in gusty weather, when the wind has frequently a downward trend, which has the effect of cambering the surface the wrong way about, and placing the machine flat on the ground. Oiled or specially prepared silk of the lightest kind should be used for surfacing the aerofoils. Some form of keel, or fin, is essential to assist in keeping the machine in a straight course, combined with a rudder and universally jointed elevator.

The manner of winding up the propellers has already been referred to (see chap. iii., § 9). A winder is essential.

Another form of aerofoil is one of wood (as in Clarke's flyers) or metal, such a machine relying more on the swiftness of its flight than on its duration. In this the gearing would possibly not be so advantageous—but experiment alone could decide.

The weight of the machine would require to be an absolute minimum, and everything not absolutely essential omitted.

It is quite possible to build a twin-screw model on one central stick alone; but the isosceles triangular form of framework, with two propellers at the base corners, and the rubber motors running along the two sides and terminating at the vertex, is preferred by most model makers. It entails, of course, extra weight. A light form of skid, made of steel pianoforte wire, should be used. As to the weight and size of the model, the now famous "one-ouncers" have made some long flights of over 300 yards[43]; but the machine claiming the record, half a mile,[44] weighs about 10 oz. And apart from this latter consideration altogether the writer is inclined to think that from 5 oz. to 10 oz. is likely to prove the most suitable. It is not too large to experiment with without difficulty, nor is it so small as to require the skill of a jeweller almost to build the necessary mechanism. The propeller speed has already been discussed (*see* ch. v., § 15). The model will, of course, be flown with the wind. The *total* length of the model should be at least twice the span of the main aerofoil.

CHAPTER IX.

THE STEERING OF THE MODEL.

§ 1. Of all the various sections of model aeroplaning that which is the least satisfactory is the above.

The torque of the propeller naturally exerts a twisting or tilting effect upon the model as a whole, the effect of which is to cause it to fly in (roughly speaking) a circular course, the direction depending on whether the pitch of the screw be a right or left handed one. There are various devices by which the torque may be (approximately) got rid of.

§ 2. In the case of a monoplane, by not placing the rod carrying the rubber motor in the exact centre of the main aerofoil, but slightly to one side, the exact position to be determined by experiment.

In a biplane the same result is obtained by keeping the rod in the centre, but placing the bracket carrying the bearing in which the propeller shaft runs at right angles horizontally to the rod to obtain the same effect.

§ 3. The most obvious solution of the problem is to use *two* equal propellers (as in the Wright biplane) of equal and opposite pitch, driven by two rubber motors of equal strength.

Theoretically this idea is perfect. In practice it is not so. It is quite possible, of course, to use two rubber motors of an equal number of strands (equality should be first tested by *weighing*). It should be possible to obtain two propellers of equal and opposite pitch, etc., and it is also possible to give the rubber motors the same number of turns. In practice one is always wound up before the other. This is the first mistake. They should be wound up *at the same time*, using a double winder made for the purpose.

The fact that this is *not* done is quite sufficient to give an unequal torsion. The friction in both cases must also be exactly equal. Both propellers must be released at exactly the same instant.

Supposing *all* these conditions fulfilled (in practice they never are), supposing also the propellers connected by gearing (prohibitive on account of the weight), and the air quite calm (which it never is), then the machine should and undoubtedly would *fly straight*.

For steering purposes by winding up one propeller *many more times* than the other, the aeroplane can generally speaking be steered to the right or left; but from what I have both seen and tried twin-screw model aeroplanes are *not* the success they are often made out to be, and they are much more troublesome to deal with, in spite of what some say to the contrary.

The solution of the problem of steering by the use of two propellers is only partially satisfactory and reliable, in fact, it is no solution at all.[45] The torque of the propeller and consequent tilting of the aeroplane is not the only cause at work diverting the machine from its course.

§ 4. As it progresses through the air it is constantly meeting air currents of varying velocity and direction, all tending to make the model deviate more or less from its course; the best way, in fact, the only way, to successfully overcome such is by means of *speed*, by giving the aeroplane a high velocity, not of ten or twelve to fifteen miles an hour, as is usual in built up fabric-covered aerofoils, but a velocity of twenty to thirty miles an hour, attainable only in models (petrol or steam driven) or by means of wooden or metal aerofoils.

§ 5. Amongst devices used for horizontal steering are vertical "FINS." These should be placed in the rear above the centre of gravity. They should not be large, and can be made of fabric tightly stretched over a wire frame, or of a piece of sheet magnalium or aluminium, turning on a pivot at the front edge, adjustment being made by simply twisting the fin round to the desired angle. As to the size, think of rudder and the size of a boat, but allow for the difference of medium. The frame carrying the pivot and fin should be made to slide along the rod or backbone of the model in order to find the most efficient position.

§ 6. Steering may also be attempted by means of little balancing tips, or ailerons, fixed to or near the main aerofoil, and pivoted (either centrally or otherwise) in such a manner that they can be rotated one in one direction (tilted) and the other in the other (dipped), so as to raise one side and depress the other.

§ 7. The model can also be steered by giving it a cant to one side by weighting the tip of the aerofoil on that side on which it is desired it should turn, but this method is both clumsy and "weighty."

§ 8. Another way is by means of the elevator; and this method, since it entails no additional surfaces entailing extra resistance and weight, is perhaps the most satisfactory of all.

It is necessary that the elevator be mounted on some kind of universal joint, in order that it may not only be "tipped" or "dipped," but also canted sideways for horizontal steering.

§ 9. A vertical fin in the rear, or something in the nature of a "keel," i.e. a vertical fin running down the backbone of the machine, greatly assists this movement.

If the model be of the tractor screw and tail (Blériot) type, then the above remarks *re* elevator apply *mutatis mutandis* to the tail.

§ 10. It is of the most vital importance that the propeller torque should be, as far as possible, correctly balanced. This can be tested by balancing the model transversely on a knife edge, winding up the propeller, and allowing it to run down, and adjusting matters until the torque and compensatory apparatus balance. As the torque varies the mean should be used.

In the case of twin propellers, suspend the model by its centre of gravity, wind up the propellers, and when running down if the model is drawn forward without rotation the thrust is equal; if not adjustment must be made till it does. The easiest way to do this *may* be by placing one propeller, the one giving the greater thrust, slightly nearer the centre.

In the case of two propellers rotating in opposite directions (by suitable gearing) on the common centre of two axes, one of the axes being, of course, hollow, and turning on the other—the rear propeller working in air already driven back by the other will require a coarser pitch or larger diameter to be equally efficient.

CHAPTER X.

THE LAUNCHING OF THE MODEL.

§ 1. Generally speaking, the model should be launched into the air *against the wind.*

§ 2. It should (theoretically) be launched into the air with a velocity equal to that with which it flies. If it launch with a velocity in excess of that it becomes at once unstable and has to "settle down" before assuming its normal line of flight. If the velocity be insufficient, it may be unable to "pick up" its requisite velocity in time to prevent its falling to the ground. Models with wooden aerofoils and a high aspect ratio designed for swift flying, such as the well-known Clarke flyers, require to be practically "hurled" into the air.

Other fabric-covered models capable of sustentation at a velocity of 8 to 10 miles an hour, may just be "released."

§ 3. Light "featherweight" models designed for long flights when travelling with the wind should be launched with it. They will not advance into it—if there be anything of a breeze—but, if well designed, just "hover," finally sinking to earth on an even keel. Many ingenious pieces of apparatus have been designed to mechanically launch the model into the air. Fig. 50 is an illustration of a very simple but effective one.

§ 4. For large size power-driven models, unless provided with a chassis and wheels to enable them to run along and rise from the ground under their own power, the launching is a problem of considerable difficulty.

§ 5. In the case of rubber-driven models desired to run along and rise from the ground under their own power, this rising must be accomplished quickly and in a short space. A model requiring a 50 ft. run is useless, as the motor would be practically run out by that time. Ten or twelve feet is the limit; now, in order to rise quickly the machine must be light and carry considerable surface, or, in other words, its velocity of sustentation must be a low one.

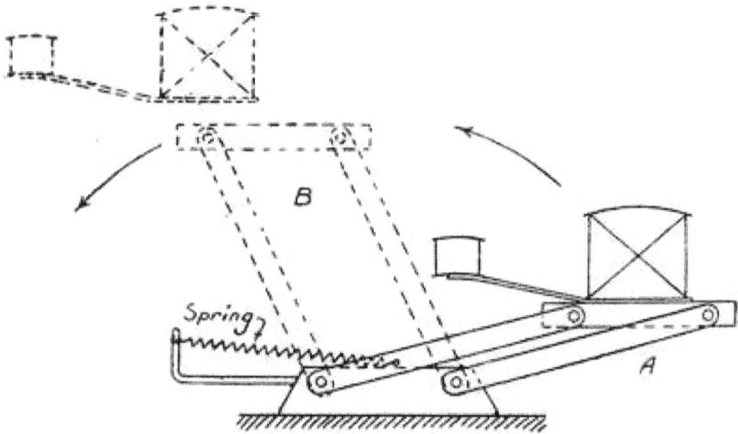

FIG. 50.—MR. POYNTER'S LAUNCHING APPARATUS.
[*REPRODUCED BY PERMISSION FROM THE "MODEL ENGINEER."*]

§ 6. It will not do to tip up the elevator to a large angle to make it rise quickly, because when once off the ground the angle of the elevator is wrong for actual flight and the model will probably turn a somersault and land on its back. I have often seen this happen. If the elevator be set at an increased angle to get it to rise quickly, then what is required is a little mechanical device which sets the elevator at its proper flight angle when it leaves the ground. Such a device does not present any great mechanical difficulties; and I leave it to the mechanical ingenuity of my readers to devise a simple little device which shall maintain the elevator at a comparatively large angle while the model is on the ground, but allowing of this angle being reduced when free flight is commenced.

§ 7. The propeller most suitable to "get the machine off the ground" is one giving considerable statical thrust. A small propeller of fine pitch quickly starts a machine, but is not, of course, so efficient when the model is in actual flight. A rubber motor is not at all well adapted for the purpose just discussed.

§ 8. Professor Kress uses a polished plank (down which the models slip on cane skids) to launch his models.

§ 9. When launching a twin-screw model the model should be held by each propeller, or to speak more correctly, the two brackets holding the bearings in which the propeller shafts run should be held one in each hand in such a way, of course, as to prevent the propellers from revolving. Hold the machine vertically downwards, or, if too large for this, allow the nose to rest slightly on the ground; raise (or swing) the machine up into the air until a little more than horizontal position is attained, and boldly push the machine into the air (moving forward if necessary) and release both brackets and screws simultaneously.[46]

§ 10. In launching a model some prefer to allow the propellers to revolve for a few moments (a second, say) *before* actually launching, contending that this gives a steadier initial flight. This is undoubtedly the case, see note on page 111.

§ 11. In any case, unless trying for a height prize, do not point the nose of the machine right up into the air with the idea that you will thereby obtain a better flight.

Launch it horizontally, or at a very small angle of inclination. When requiring a model to run along a field or a lawn and rise therefrom this is much facilitated by using a little strip of smooth oilcloth on which it can run. Remember that swift flying wooden and metal models require a high initial velocity, particularly if of large size and weight. If thrown steadily and at the proper angle they can scarcely be overthrown.

CHAPTER XI.

HELICOPTER MODELS.

§ 1. There is no difficulty whatever about making successful model helicopters, whatever there may be about full-sized machines.

§ 2. The earliest flying models were helicopters. As early as 1796 Sir George Cayley constructed a perfectly successful helicopter model (see ch. iii.); it should be noticed the screws were superimposed and rotated in opposite directions.

§ 3. In 1842 a Mr. Phillips constructed a successful power-driven model helicopter. The model was made entirely of metal, and when complete and charged weighed 2 lb. It consisted of a boiler or steam generator and four fans supported between eight arms. The fans had an inclination to the horizon of 20°, and through the arms the steam rushed on the principle of Hero's engines (Barker's Mill Principle probably). By the escape of steam from the arms the fans were caused to revolve with immense energy, so much so that the model rose to an immense altitude and flew across two fields before it alighted. The motive power employed was obtained from the combustion of charcoal, nitre and gypsum, as used in the original fire annihilator; the products of combustion mixing with water in the boiler and forming gas-charged steam, which was delivered at high pressure from the extremities of the eight arms.[47] This model and its flight (fully authenticated) is full of interest and should not be lost sight of, as in all probability being the first model actuated by steam which actually flew.

The helicopter is but a particular phase of the aeroplane.

§ 4. The simplest form of helicopter is that in which the torque of the propeller is resisted by a vertical loose fabric plane, so designed as itself to form a propeller, rotating in the opposite direction. These little toys can be bought at any good toy shop from about 6d. to 1s. Supposing we desire to construct a helicopter of a more ambitious and scientific character, possessing a vertically rotating propeller or propellers for horizontal propulsion, as well as horizontally rotating propellers for lifting purposes.

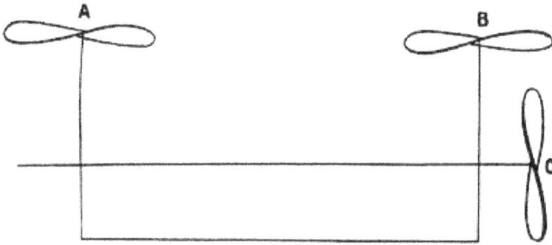

Fig. 51.—Incorrect Way of Arranging Screws.

§ 5. There is one essential point that must be carefully attended to, and that is, *that the horizontal propulsive thrust must be in the same plane as the vertical lift*, or the only effect will be to cause our model to turn somersaults. I speak from experience.

When the horizontally revolving propellers are driven in a horizontal direction their "lifting" powers will be materially increased, as they will (like an ordinary aeroplane) be advancing on to fresh undisturbed air.

§ 6. I have not for ordinary purposes advocated very light weight wire framework fabric-covered screws, but in a case like this where the thrust from the propeller has to be more than the total weight of the machine, these might possibly be used with advantage.

§ 7. Instead of using two long vertical rods as well as one long horizontal one for the rubber strands, we might dispense with the two vertical ones altogether and use light gearing to turn the torque action through a right angle for the lifting screws, and use three separate horizontal rubber strands for the three propellers on a suitable light horizontal framework. Such should result in a considerable saving of weight.

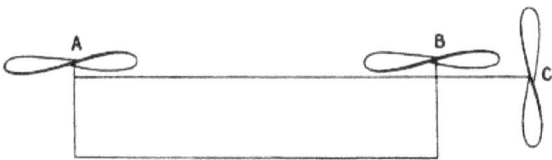

FIG. 52.—CORRECT MANNER.
A, B, C = SCREWS.

§ 8. The model would require something in the nature of a vertical fin or keel to give the sense of direction. Four propellers, two for "lift" and two for "drift," would undoubtedly be a better arrangement.

CHAPTER XII.

EXPERIMENTAL RECORDS.

A model flying machine being a scientific invention and not a toy, every devotee to the science should make it his or her business to keep, as far as they are able, accurate and scientific records. For by such means as this, and the making known of the same, can a *science* of model aeroplaning be finally evolved. The following experimental entry forms, left purposely blank to be filled in by the reader, are intended as suggestions only, and can, of course, be varied at the reader's discretion. When you *have* obtained carefully established data, do not keep them to yourself, send them along to one of the aeronautical journals. Do not think them valueless; if carefully arranged they cannot be that, and may be very valuable.

EXPERIMENTAL DATA.
FORM I.

Model	Weight	Area of Supporting Surface	Aspect Ratio	Average Length of Flight in Feet	Maximum Flight	Time of Flight A. average M. maximum		Kind and Direction of Wind	Direction of Flight	Camber	Angle of Inclination of Main Aerofoil to Line of Flight
						A	M				
1											
2											
3											
4											
5											
6											
7											
8											
9											
10											
11											
12											

FORM I.*continued.*

Model	Weight of (Rubber) Motor	Kind of Rubber Flat, Square or Round	Length in Inches and Number of Strands	Number of Turns	Condition at End of Flight	Number of Propellors and Diameter		Number of Blades	Disc Area and Pitch		Percentage of Slip	Thrust	Torque in Inch-Ounces
						No.	Diam.		DiscA.	Pitch			
1													
2													
3													
4													
5													
6													
7													
8													
9													
10													
11													
12													

CHAPTER XIII.

MODEL FLYING COMPETITIONS.

§ 1. From time to time flying competitions are arranged for model aeroplanes. Sometimes these competitions are entirely open, but more generally they are arranged by local clubs with both closed and open events.

No two programmes are probably exactly alike, but the following may be taken as fairly representative:—

1. Longest flight measured in a straight line (sometimes both with and against the wind).[48]

2. Stability (both longitudinal and transverse).

3. Longest glide when launched from a given height without power, but with motor and propeller attached.

4. Steering.

5. Greatest height.

6. The best all-round model, including, in addition to the above, excellence in building.

Generally so many "points" or marks are given for each test, and the model whose aggregate of points makes the largest total wins the prize; or more than one prize may be offered—

One for the longest flight.

One for the swiftest flight over a measured distance.

One for the greatest height.

One for stability and steering.

And one for the best all-round model.

The models are divided into classes:—

§ 2. *Aero Models Association's Classification, etc.*

A.	Models of	1 sq. ft.	surface	and	under.
B.	"	2 sq. ft.	"		"
C.	"	4 sq. ft.	"		"
D.	"	8 sq. ft.	"		"
E.	"	over 8 sq. ft.			

All surfaces, whether vertical, horizontal, or otherwise, to be calculated together for the above classification.

All round efficiency—marks or points as percentages:—

Distance	40	per cent.
Stability	35	"
Directional control	15	"
Gliding angle	10	"[49]

Two prizes:—

One for length of flight.

One for all-round efficiency (marked as above).

Every competitor to be allowed three trials in each competition, the best only to count.

All flights to be measured in a straight line from the starting to the landing point.

Repairs may be made during the competition at the direction of the judges.[50]

There are one or two other points where flights are *not* made with and against the wind. The competitors are usually requested to start their models from within a given circle of (say) six feet diameter, and fly them *in any direction* they please.

"Gliding angle" means that the model is allowed to fall from a height (say) of 20 ft.

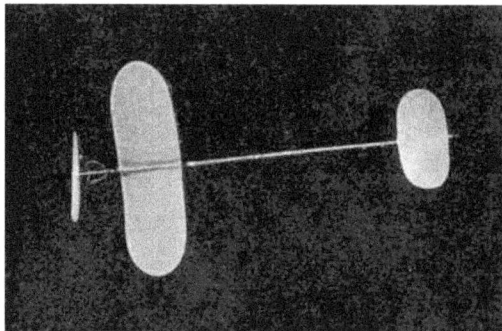

FIG. 53.—MODEL DESIGNED AND CONSTRUCTED BY THE AUTHOR FOR "GREATEST HEIGHT."
A very lightly built model with a very low aspect ratio, and screw giving a very powerful dynamic thrust, and carrying rather a large amount of rubber. Climbs in left-handed spirals.

"Directional control," that the model is launched in some specified direction, and must pass as near as possible over some indicated point.

The models are practically always launched by hand.

§ 3. Those who desire to win prizes at such competitions would do well to keep the following points well in mind.

1. The distance is always measured in a straight line. It is absolutely essential that your model should be capable of flying (approximately) straight. To see, as I have done, model after model fly quite 150 to 200 yards and finish within 50 yards of the starting-point (credited flight 50 yards) is useless, and a severe strain on one's temper and patience.

FIG. 54.—THE GAMAGE CHALLENGE CUP.
OPEN COMPETITION FOR LONGEST FLIGHT. CRYSTAL PALACE, JULY 27.
WON BY MR. E.W. TWINING.

FIG. 55.—MEDAL WON BY THE AUTHOR IN THE SAME COMPETITION.

2. Always enter more than one model, there nearly always is an entrance fee; never mind the extra shilling or so. Go in to win.

3. It is not necessary that these models should be replicas of one another. On some days a light fabric-covered model might stand the best chance; on another day, a swift flying wooden or metal aerofoil.

Against the wind the latter have an immense advantage; also if the day be a "gusty" one.[51]

4. Always make it a point of arriving early on the ground, so that you can make some trial flights beforehand. Every ground has its local peculiarities of air currents, etc.

5. Always be ready in time, or you may be disqualified. If you are flying a twin-screw model use a special winder, so that both propellers are wound up at the same time, and take a competent friend with you as assistant.

6. For all-round efficiency nothing but a good all-round model, which can be absolutely relied on to make a dozen (approximately) equivalent flights, is any good.

7. In an open distance competition, unless you have a model which you can rely on to make a *minimum* flight of 200 yards, do not enter unless you know for certain that none of the "crack" flyers will be present.

8. Do not neglect the smallest detail likely to lead to success; be prepared with spare parts, extra rubber, one or two handy tools, wire, thread, etc. Before a lecture, that prince of experimentalists, Faraday, was always careful

to see that the stoppers of all the bottles were loose, so that there should be no delay or mishap.

9. If the rating of the model be by "weight" (1 oz., 2 oz., 4 oz., etc.) and not area, use a model weighing from 10 oz. to a pound.

10. If there is a greatest height prize, a helicopter model should win it.[52] (The writer has attained an altitude of between three and four hundred feet with such.) The altitude was arrived at by observation, not guesswork.

11. It is most important that your model should be able to "land" without damage, and, as far as possible, on an even keel; do not omit some form of "skid" or "shock-absorber" with the idea of saving weight, more especially if your model be a biplane, or the number of flights may be restricted to the number "one."

12. Since the best "gliding" angle and "flying" angle are not the same, being, say, 7° in the former case and 1°-3°, say, in the latter, an adjustable angle might in some cases be advantageous.

13. Never turn up at a competition with a model only just finished and practically untested which you have flown only on the morning of the competition, using old rubber and winding to 500 turns; result, a flight of 250 yards, say. Arrived on the competition ground you put on new rubber and wind to 750 turns, and expect a flight of a quarter of a mile at least; result 70 yards, *measured in a straight line* from the starting-point.

14. Directional control is the most difficult problem to overcome with any degree of success under all adverse conditions, and 15 per cent., in the writer's opinion, is far too low a percentage; by directional I include flying in a straight line; personally I would mark for all-round efficiency: (A) distance and stability, 50 per cent.; (B) directional control, 30 per cent.; (C) duration of flight, 20 per cent. In A the competitor would launch his model *in any direction*; in B as directed by the judges. No separate flights required for C.

CHAPTER XIV.
USEFUL NOTES, TABLES, FORMULÆ, ETC.

§ 1. COMPARATIVE VELOCITIES.

Miles per hr.		Feet per sec.		Metres per sec.
10	=	14·7	=	4·470
15	=	22	=	6·705
20	=	29·4	=	8·940
25	=	36·7	=	11·176
30	=	44	=	13·411
35	=	51·3	=	15·646

§ 2. A metre = 39·37079 inches.

In order to convert—

Metres into	inches	multiply by	39·37
"	feet	"	3·28
"	yards	"	1·09
"	miles	"	0·0006214

Miles per hour into	ft. per min.	multiply by	88·0
"	min. into ft. per sec.	"	88·0
"	hr. into kilometres per hr.	"	1·6093
"	" metres per sec.	"	0·44702
Pounds into	grammes	"	453·593
"	kilogrammes	"	0·4536

§ 3. Total surface of a cylinder = circumference of base × height + 2 area of base.

Area of a circle = square of diameter × 0·7854.

Area of a circle = square of rad. × 3·14159.

Area of an ellipse = product of axes × 0·7854.

Circumference of a circle = diameter × 3·14159.

Solidity of a cylinder = height × area of base.

Area of a circular ring = sum of diameters × difference of diameters × 0·7854.

For the area of a sector of a circle the rule is:—As 360 : number of degrees in the angle of the sector :: area of the sector : area of circle.

To find the area of a segment less than a semicircle:—Find the area of the sector which has the same arc, and subtract the area of the triangle formed by the radii and the chord.

The areas of corresponding figures are as the squares of corresponding lengths.

§ 4.

1 mile   = 1·609 kilometres.

1 kilometre = 1093 yards.

1 oz.   = 28·35 grammes.

1 lb.   = 453·59   "

1 lb.   = 0·453 kilogrammes

28 lb.   = 12·7   "

112 lb.   = 50·8   "

2240 lb.   = 1016   "

1 kilogram = 2·2046 lb.

1 gram   = 0·0022 lb.

1 sq. in.   = 645 sq. millimetres.

1 sq. ft.   = 0·0929 sq. metres.

1 sq. yard = 0·836   "

1 sq. metre = 10·764 sq. ft.

§ 5. One atmosphere = 14·7 lb. per sq. in. = 2116 lb. per sq. ft. = 760 millimetres of mercury.

A column of water 2·3 ft. high corresponds to a pressure of 1 lb. per sq. in.

1 H.P. = 33,000 ft.-lb. per min. = 746 watts.

Volts × amperes = watts.

$\pi = 3\cdot1416$. $g = 32\cdot182$ ft. per sec. at London.

§ 6. TABLE OF EQUIVALENT INCLINATIONS.

Rise.	Angle in Degs.
1 in 30	1·91
1 " 25	2·29
1 " 20	2·87
1 " 18	3·18
1 " 16	3·58
1 " 14	4·09
1 " 12	4·78
1 " 10	5·73
1 " 9	6·38
1 " 8	7·18
1 " 7	8·22
1 " 6	9·6
1 " 5	11·53
1 " 4	14·48
1 " 3	19·45
1 " 2	30·00
1 " $\sqrt{2}$	45·00

§ 7. TABLE OF SKIN FRICTION.
Per sq. ft. for various speeds and surface lengths.

Velocity of Wind	1 ft. Plane	2 ft. Plane	4 ft. Plane	8 ft. Plane
10	·00112	·00105	·00101	·000967
15	·00237	·00226	·00215	·00205
20	·00402	·00384	·00365	·00349
25	·00606	·00579	·00551	·00527
30	·00850	·00810	·00772	·00736
35	·01130	·0108	·0103	·0098

This table is based on Dr. Zahm's experiments and the equation

$$f = 0.00000778 l^{0.07} v^{1.85}$$

Where f = skin friction per sq. ft.; l = length of surface; v = velocity in feet per second.

In a biplane model the head resistance is probably from twelve to fourteen times the skin friction; in a racing monoplane from six to eight times.

§ 8. TABLE I.—(METALS).

Material	Specific Gravity	Elasticity E[A]	Tenacity per sq. in.
Magnesium	1·74		22,000-32,000
Magnalium[B]	2·4-2·57	10·2	
Aluminium-Copper[C]	2·82		54,773
Aluminium	2·6	11·1	26,535
Iron	7·7 (about)	29	54,000
Steel	7·8 (about)	32	100,000

Brass	7·8-8·4	15	17,500
Copper	8·8	36	33,000
Mild Steel	7·8	30	60,000

[A] E in millions of lb. per sq.in.
[B] Magnalium is an alloy of magnesium and aluminium.
[C] Aluminium 94 per cent., copper 6 per cent. (the best percentage), a 6 per cent. alloy thereby doubles the tenacity of pure aluminium with but 5 per cent. increase of density.

§ 9. TABLE II.—WIND PRESSURES.

$$p = kv^2.$$

k coefficient (mean value taken) ·003 (miles per hour) = 0·0016 ft. per second. p = pressure in lb. per sq. ft. v = velocity of wind.

Miles per hr.	Ft. per sec.	Lb. per sq. ft.
10	14·7	0·300
12	17·6	0·432
14	20·5	0·588
16	23·5	0·768

Miles per hr.	Ft. per sec.	Lb. per sq. ft.
18	26·4	0·972
20	29·35	1·200
25	36·7	1·875
30	43·9	2·700
35	51·3	3·675

§ 10. Representing normal pressure on a plane surface by 1; pressure on a rod (round section) is 0·6; on a symmetrical elliptic cross section (axes 2:1) is 0·2 (approx.). Similar shape, but axes 6:1, and edges sharpened (*see* ch. ii.,

§ 5), is only 0·05, or 1/20, and for the body of minimum resistance (*see* ch. ii., § 4) about 1/24.

§ 11. TABLE III.—LIFT AND DRIFT.

On a well shaped aerocurve or correctly designed cambered surface. Aspect ratio 4·5.

Inclination. Ratio Lift to Drift.

0°	19:1
2·87°	15:1
3·58°	16:1
4·09°	14:1
4·78°	12:1
5·73°	9·6:1
7·18°	7·9:1

Wind velocity 40 miles per hour. (The above deduced from some experiments of Sir Hiram Maxim.)

At a velocity of 30 miles an hour a good aerocurve should lift 21 oz. to 24 oz. per sq. ft.

§ 12. TABLE IV.—LIFT AND DRIFT.

On a plane aerofoil.

$$N = P(2 \sin \alpha / 1 + \sin^2 \alpha)$$

Inclination. Ratio Lift to Drift.

1°	58·3:1
2°	29·2:1
3°	19·3:1
4°	14·3:1
5°	11·4:1

6°	9·5:1
7°	8·0:1
8°	7·0:1
9°	6·3:1
10°	5·7:1

$$P = 2kd\,AV^2 \sin \alpha.$$

A useful formula for a single plane surface. P = pressure supporting the plane in pounds per square foot, k a constant = 0·003 in miles per hour, d = the density of the air.

A = the area of the plane, V relative velocity of translation through the air, and α the angle of flight.

Transposing we have

$$AV^2 = P/(2kd \sin \alpha)$$

If P and α are constants; then AV^2 = a constant or area is inversely as velocity squared. Increase of velocity meaning diminished supporting surface (*and so far as supporting surface goes*), diminished resistance and skin friction. It must be remembered, however, that while the work of sustentation diminishes with the speed, the work of penetration varies as the cube of the speed.

§ 13. TABLE V.—TIMBER.

Material	Specific Gravity	Weight per Cub. Ft. in Lb.	Strength per Sq. In. in Lb.	Ultimate Breaking Load (Lb.) Span 1'×1"×1"	Relative Resilience in Bending	Modulus of Elasticity in Millions of Lb. per Sq. In. for Bending	Relative Value. Bending Strength compared with Weight
Ash	·79	43-52	14,000-17,000	622	4·69	1·55	13·0
Bamboo		25[A]	6300[A]		3·07	3·20	
Beech	·69	43	10,000-12,000	850		1·65	19·8
Birch	·71	45	15,000	550		3·28	12·2
Box	1·28	80	20,000-23,000	815			10·2
Cork	·24	15					
Fir (Norway Spruce)	·51	32	9,000-11,000	450	3·01	1·70	14·0
American Hickory		49	11,000	800	3·47	2·40	16·3
Honduras Mahogany	·56	35	20,000	750	3·40	1·60	21·4
Maple	·68	44	10,600	750			17·0
merican White Pine	·42	25	11,800	450	2·37	1·39	18·0
ombardy Poplar		24	7,000	550	2·89	0·77	22·9
nerican Yellow Poplar		44	10,000		3·63	1·40	
Satinwood	·96	60		1,033			17·2
Spruce	·50	31	12,400	450			14·5
ular Ash. t =1/8 d		47			3·50	1·55	

t = thickness: d = diameter.
[A]Given elsewhere as 55 and 22,500 (t = 1/3 d), evidently regarded as solid.

§ 14.—Formula connecting the Weight Lifted in Pounds per Square Foot and the Velocity.—The empirical formula

$$W = (V^2C)/g$$

Where W = weight lifted in lb. per sq. ft.
V = velocity in ft. per sec.
C = a constant = 0·025.
g = 32·2, or 32 approx.

may be used for a thoroughly efficient model. This gives (approximately)

1 lb.   per sq. ft.   lift at   25   miles an hour.

21 oz.   "   "   30   "

6 oz.   "   "   15   "

4 oz.   "   "   12   "

2·7 oz.   "   "   10   "

Remember the results work out in feet per second. To convert (approximately) into miles per hour multiply by 2/3.

§ 15. Formula connecting Models of Similar Design, but Different Weights.

$$D \propto \sqrt{W}.$$

or in models of *similar design* the distances flown are proportional to the square roots of the weights. (Derived from data obtained from Clarke's flyers.)

For models from 1 oz. to 24-30 oz. the formula appears to hold very well. For heavier models it appears to give the heavier model rather too great a distance.

Since this was deduced a 1 oz. Clarke model of somewhat similar design but longer rubber motor has flown 750 ft. at least; it is true the design is not, strictly speaking, similar, but not too much reliance must be placed on the above. The record for a 1 oz. model to date is over 300 yards (with the wind, of course), say 750 ft. in calm air.

§ 16. Power and Speed.—The following formula, given by Mr. L. Blin Desbleds, between these is—

$$W/W_0 = 3v_0/4v + \frac{1}{4}(v/v_0)^3.$$

Where v_0 = speed of minimum power
W_0 = work done at speed v_0.
W = work done at speed v.

Making $v = 2v_0$, i.e. doubling the speed of minimum power, and substituting, we have finally

$$W = (2^3/8)W_0$$

i.e. the speed of an aeroplane can be doubled by using a power $2^3/8$ times as great as the original one. The "speed of minimum power" being the speed at which the aeroplane must travel for the minimum expenditure of power.

§ 17. The thrust of the propeller has evidently to balance the

Aerodynamic resistance = R
The head resistance (including skin friction) = S

Now according to Renard's theorem, the power absorbed by R + S is a minimum when

$$S = R/3.$$

Having built a model, then, in which the total resistance

$$= {}^4/_3R.$$

This is the thrust which the propeller should be designed to give. Now supposing the propeller's efficiency to be 80 per cent., then P—the minimum propulsion power

$$= {}^4/_3R \times {}^{100}/_{80} \times {}^{100}/_{75} \times v.$$

Where 25 per cent. is the slip of the screw, v the velocity of the aeroplane.

§ 18. **To determine experimentally the Static Thrust of a Propeller.—** Useful for models intended to raise themselves from the ground under their own power, and for helicopters.

The easiest way to do this is as follows: Mount the propeller on the shaft of an electric motor, of sufficient power to give the propeller 1000 to 1500 revolutions per minute; a suitable accumulator or other source of electric energy will be required, a speedometer or speed counter, also a voltmeter and ammeter.

Place the motor in a pair of scales or on a suitable spring balance (the former is preferable), the axis of the motor vertical, with the propeller attached. Rotate the propeller so that the air current is driven *upwards*. When the correct speed (as indicated by the speed counter) has been attained, notice the difference in the readings if a spring balance be used, or, if a pair of scales, place weights in the scale pan until the downward thrust of the propeller is exactly balanced. This gives you the thrust in ounces or pounds.

Note carefully the voltage and amperage, supposing it is 8 volts and 10 amperes = 80 watts.

Remove the propeller and note the volts and amperes consumed to run the motor alone, i.e. to excite itself, and overcome friction and air resistance; suppose this to be 8 volts and 2 amperes = 16; the increased load when the propeller is on is therefore

$$80 - 16 = 64 \text{ watts.}$$

All this increased power is not, however, expended on the propeller.

The lost power in the motor increases as C^2R.

R = resistance of armature and C = current. If we deduct 10 per cent. for this then the propeller is actually driven by 56 watts.

Now 746 watts = 1 h.p.

$$\therefore {}^{56}/_{746} = {}^1/_{13} \text{ h.p. approx.}$$

at the observed number of revolutions per minute.

§ 19. N.B.—The h.p. required to drive a propeller varies as the cube of the revolutions.

Proof.—Double the speed of the screw, then it strikes the air twice as hard; it also strikes twice as much air, and the motor has to go twice as fast to do it.

§ 20. To compare one model with another the formula

$$\text{Weight} \times \text{velocity (in ft. per sec.)} / \text{horse-power}$$

is sometimes useful.

§ 21. **A Horse-power** is 33,000 lb. raised one foot in one minute, or 550 lb. one foot in one second.

A clockwork spring raised 1 lb. through 4½ ft. in 3 seconds. What is its h.p.?

$$\text{1 lb. through 4½ ft. in 3 seconds}$$
$$\text{is 1 lb. " 90 ft. " 1 minute.}$$

$$\therefore \text{Work done is 90 ft.-lb.}$$
$$= {}^{90}/_{33000} = 0 \cdot 002727 \text{ h.p.}$$

The weight of the spring was 6¾ oz. (this is taken from an actual experiment), i.e. this motor develops power at the rate of $0 \cdot 002727$ h.p. for 3½ seconds only.

§ 22. **To Ascertain the H.P. of a Rubber Motor.** Supposing a propeller wound up to 250 turns to run down in 15 seconds, i.e. at a mean speed of 1200 revolutions per minute or 20 per second. Suppose the mean thrust to be 2 oz., and let the pitch of the propeller be 1 foot. Then the number of foot-pounds of energy developed

$$= 2 \text{ oz.} \times 1200 \text{ revols.} \times 1 \text{ ft. (pitch)} / 16 \text{ oz.}$$

$$= 150 \text{ ft.-lb. per minute.}$$

But the rubber motor runs down in 15 seconds.
$\therefore$ Energy really developed is

$$= 150 \times 15 / 60 = 37 \cdot 5 \text{ ft.-lb.}$$

The motor develops power at rate of ${}^{150}/_{33000} = 0 \cdot 004545$ h.p., but for 15 seconds only.

§ 23. **Foot-pounds of Energy in a Given Weight of Rubber** (experimental determination of).

Length of rubber   36 yds.

Weight   "   2 $7/16$ oz .

Number of turns   = 200.

12 oz. were raised 19 ft. in 5 seconds.
i.e. ¾ lb. was raised 19 × 12 ft. in 1 minute.
i.e. 1 lb. was raised 19 × 3 × 3 ft. in 1 minute.
= 171 ft. in 1 minute.

i.e. 171 ft.-lb. of energy per minute. But actual time was 5 seconds.

∴ Actual energy developed by 2-7/16 oz. of rubber of 36 yards, i.e. 36 strands 1 yard each at 200 turns is

$$= {}^{171}/_{12} \text{ ft.-lb.}$$
$$= 14¼ \text{ ft.-lb.}$$

This allows nothing for friction or turning the axle on which the cord was wound. Ball bearings were used; but the rubber was not new and twenty turns were still unwound at the end of the experiment. Now allowing for friction, etc. being the same as on an actual model, we can take ¾ of a ft.-lb. for the unwound amount and estimate the total energy as 15 ft.-lb. as a minimum. The energy actually developed being at the rate of 0·0055 h.p., or $^1/_{200}$ of a h.p. if supposed uniform.

§ 24. The actual energy derivable from 1 lb. weight of rubber is stated to be 300 ft.-lb. On this basis 2-7/16 oz. should be capable of giving 45·7 ft.-lb. of energy, i.e. three times the amount given above. Now the motor-rubber not lubricated was only given 200 turns—lubricated 400 could have been given it, 600 probably before rupture—and the energy then derivable would certainly have been approximating to 45 ft.-lb., i.e. 36·25. Now on the basis of 300 ft.-lb. per lb. a weight of ½ oz. (the amount of rubber carried in "one-ouncers") gives 9 ft.-lb. of energy. Now assuming the gliding angle (including weight of propellers) to be 1 in 8; a perfectly efficient model should be capable of flying eight times as great a distance in a horizontal direction as the energy in the rubber motor would lift it vertically. Now 9 ft.-lb. of energy will lift 1 oz. 154 ft. Therefore theoretically it will drive it a distance (in yards) of

$$^{8 \times 154}/_3 = 410·6 \text{ yards.}$$

Now the greatest distance that a 1 oz. model has flown in perfectly calm air (which never exists) is not known. Flying with the wind 500 yards is claimed.

Admitting this what allowance shall we make for the wind; supposing we deduct half this, viz. 250 yards. Then, on this assumption, the efficiency of this "one ouncer" works out (in perfectly still air) at 61 per cent.

The gliding angle assumption of 1 in 8 is rather a high one, possibly too high; all the writer desires to show is the method of working out.

Mr. T.W.K. Clarke informs me that in his one-ouncers the gliding angle is about 1 in 5.

§ 25. **To Test Different Motors or Different Powers of the Same Kind of Motor.**—Test them on the same machine, and do not use different motors or different powers on different machines.

§ 26. **Efficiency of a Model.**—The efficiency of a model depends on the weight carried per h.p.

§ 27. **Efficiency of Design.**—The efficiency of some particular design depends on the amount of supporting surface necessary at a given speed.

§ 28. **Naphtha Engines**, that is, engines made on the principle of the steam engine, but which use a light spirit of petrol or similar agent in their generator instead of water with the same amount of heat, will develop twice as much energy as in the case of the ordinary steam engine.

§ 29.**Petrol Motors.**

Horse-power.	No. of Cylinders.	Weight.
¼	Single	4½ lb.
½ to ¾	"	6½ "
1½	Double	9 "

§ 30. **The Horse-power of Model Petrol Motors.**—Formula for rating of the above.

(R.P.M. = revolutions per minute.)

$$\text{H.P.} = \frac{(\text{Bore})^2 \times \text{stroke} \times \text{no. of cylinders} \times \text{R.P.M.}}{12,000}$$

If the right-hand side of the equation gives a less h.p. than that stated for some particular motor, then it follows that the h.p. of the motor has been over-estimated.

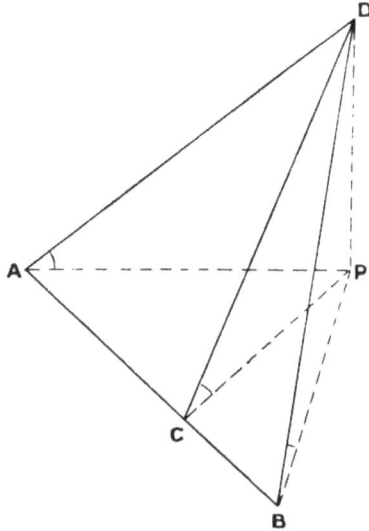

Fig. 56.

§ 30A. **Relation between Static Thrust of Propeller and Total Weight of Model.**—The thrust should be approx. = ¼ of the weight.

§ 31. **How to find the Height of an Inaccessible Object by Means of Three Observations taken on the Ground (supposed flat) in the same Straight Line.**—Let A, C, B be the angular elevations of the object D, as seen from these points, taken in the same straight line. Let the distances B C, C A and A B be a, b, c respectively. And let required height $P D = h$; then by trigonometry we have (see Fig. 56)

$$h^2 = {}^{abc}/_{(a \cot^2 A - c \cot^2 C + b \cot^2 B)}.$$

§ 32. **Formula** for calculating the I.H.P. (indicated horse-power) of a single-cylinder double-acting steam-engine.

Indicated h.p. means the h.p. actually exerted by the steam in the cylinder without taking into account engine friction. Brake h.p. or effective h.p. is the actual h.p. delivered by the crank shaft of the engine.

$$\text{I.H.P.} = {}^{2 \times S \times R \times A \times P}/_{33,000}.$$

Where S = stroke in feet.
R = revolutions per minute.
A = area of piston in inches.
P = mean pressure in lb. exerted per sq. in. on the piston.

The only difficulty is the mean effective pressure; this can be found approximately by the following rule and accompanying table.

TABLE VI.

Cut-off	Constant	Cut-off	Constant	Cut-off	Constant
$1/_6$	·566	$3/_8$	·771	$2/_3$	·917
$1/_5$	·603	·4	·789	·7	·926
$1/_4$	·659	$1/_2$	·847	$3/_4$	·937
·3	·708	·6	·895	·8	·944
$1/_3$	·743	$5/_8$	·904	$7/_8$	·951

Rule.—"Add 14·7 to gauge pressure of boiler, this giving 'absolute steam pressure,' multiply this sum by the number opposite the fraction representing the point of cut-off in the cylinder in accompanying table. Subtract 17 from the product and multiply the remainder by 0·9. The result will be very nearly the M.E.P." (R.M. de Vignier.)

APPENDIX A.

~✖✖✖~

SOME MODELS WHICH HAVE WON
MEDALS AT OPEN COMPETITIONS.

Fig. 57.—The G.P.B. Smith Model.

The model shown in Fig. 57 has won more competition medals than any other. It is a thoroughly well designed[53] and well constructed model. Originally a very slow flyer, the design has been simplified, and although by no means a fast flyer, its speed has been much accelerated. Originally a one-propeller machine, it has latterly been fitted with twin propellers, with the idea of obtaining more directional control; but in the writer's opinion, speaking from personal observation, with but little, if any, success. The steering of the model is effected by canting the elevator. Originally the machine had ailerons for the purpose, but these were removed owing, I understand, to their retarding the speed of the machine.

In every competition in which this machine has been entered it has always gained very high marks for stability.

Fig. 58.—The Gordon-Jones Dihedral Biplane.

Up to the time of writing it has not been provided with anything in the nature of fins or rudder.

Fig. 58 is a biplane very much after the type of the model just alluded to, but the one straight and one curved aerofoil surfaces are here replaced by two parallel aerofoils set on a dihedral angle. The large size of the propeller should be noted; with this the writer is in complete agreement. He has not unfortunately seen this model in actual flight.

The scientifically designed and beautifully made models illustrated in Fig. 59 are so well known that any remarks on them appear superfluous. Their efficiency, so far as their supporting area goes, is of the highest, as much as 21 oz. per square foot having been carried.

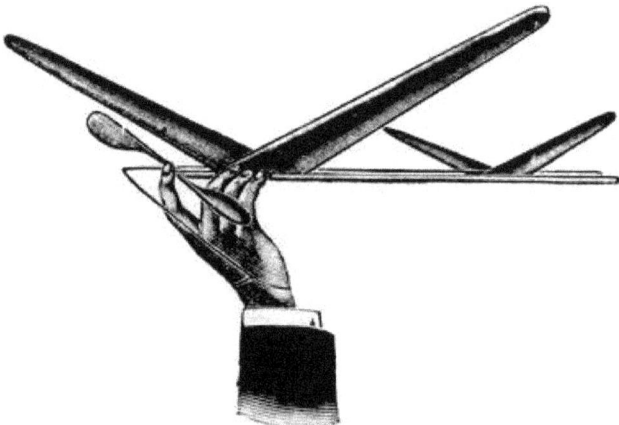

Fig. 59.—Messrs. T.W.K. Clarke and Co.'s Model Flyers.

For illustrations, etc., of the Fleming-Williams model, *see* ch. v., § 23.

(Fig. 60.) This is another well-constructed and efficient model, the shape and character of the aerofoil surfaces much resembling those of the French toy monoplane AL-MA (see § 4, ch. vii.), but they are supported and held in position by quite a different method, a neat little device enabling the front plane to become partly detached on collision with any obstacle. The model is provided with a keel (below the centre of gravity), and rudder for steering; in fact, this machine especially claims certainty of directional control. The writer has seen a number of flights by this model, but it experiences, like other models, the greatest difficulty in keeping straight if the conditions be adverse.

The model which will do this is, in his opinion, yet to be evolved. The small size of the propellers is, of course, in total disagreement with the author's ideas. All the same, the model is in many respects an excellent one, and has flown over 300 yards at the time of writing.

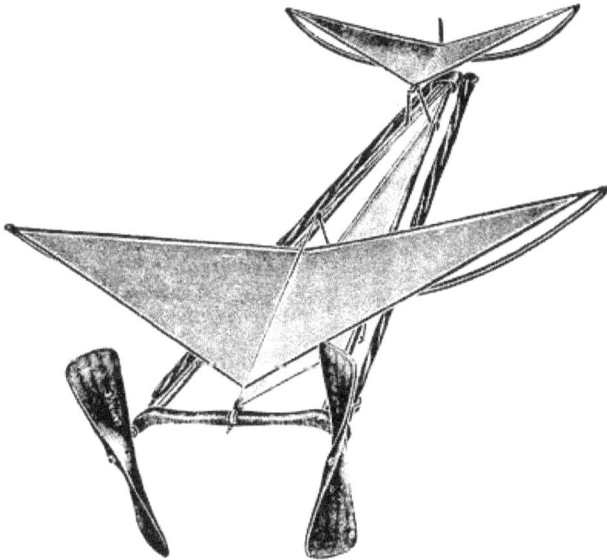

Fig. 60.—The Ding Sayers Monoplane.

More than a year ago the author made a number of models with triangular-shaped aerofoils, using umbrella ribs for the leading edge and steel piano wire for the trailing, but has latterly used aerofoils of the elongated ellipse shape.

Fig. 61 is an illustration of one of the author's latest models which won a Bronze Medal at the Long Distance Open Competition, held at the Crystal Palace on July 27, 1910, the largest and most keenly contested competition held up to that date.

The best and straightest flight against the wind was made by this model.

On the morning of the competition a flight of about 320 yards (measured in a straight line) was made on Mitcham Common, the model being launched against the wind so as to gain altitude, and then flying away with the breeze behind the writer. Duration of flight 50 seconds. The following are the chief particulars of the model:—Weight, $7\frac{1}{2}$ oz. Area of supporting surface, $1\text{-}\frac{1}{3}$ sq. ft. Total length, 4 ft. Span of main aerofoil, 25 in. Aspect ratio, 4 : 1. Diameter of propeller, 14 in. Two strand geared rubber motor, carrying altogether 28 strands of $\frac{1}{16}$ square rubber cord 43 in. long. The propeller was originally a Venna, but with the weight reduced by one-third, and considerable alteration made in its central contours. The front skid of steel pianoforte wire, the rear of jointless cane wire tipped; the rear skid was a necessity in order to protect the delicate gearing mechanism, the weight of which was reduced to a minimum.

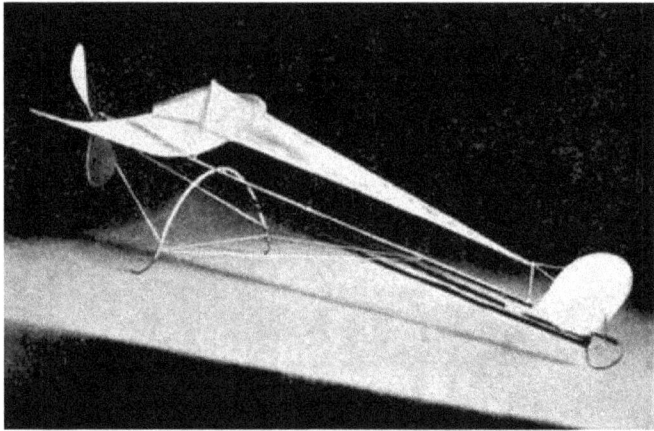

Fig. 61.—The Author's "Grasshopper" Model.

The very large diameter of the propeller should be noted, being 56 per cent. of the span. The fin, high above the centre of gravity, was so placed for transverse stability and direction. At the rear of the fin was a rudder. The small amount of rubber carried (for a long distance machine) should also be noted, especially when allowing for friction in gearing, etc.

The central rod was a penny bamboo cane, the large aerofoil of jointless cane and Hart's fabric, and the front aerofoil of steel wire surfaced with the same material.

FOOTNOTES:

[1] The smallest working steam engine that the writer has ever heard of has a net weight of 4 grains. One hundred such engines would be required to weigh one ounce. The bore being $0\cdot03$ in., and stroke $1/_{32}$ of an inch, r.p.m. 6000 per min., h.p. developed $1/_{489000}$ ("Model Engineer," July 7, 1910). When working it hums like a bee.

[2] "Aero," May 3, 1910.

[3] Part of this retardation was, of course, "increased resistance."

[4] Personally I do not recommend aluminium.—V.E.J.

[5] "Aeronautical Journal," January 1897, p. 7.

[6] *Vide* "Invention," Feb. 15, 22, and 29, 1896.

[7] Really aerofoils, since we are considering only the supporting surface.

[8] I.e., to express it as a decimal fraction of the resistance, encountered by the same plane when moving "face" instead of "edge" on.

[9] If the width be not uniform the mean width should be taken.

[10] This refers, of course, to transverse stability.

[11] See ch. vi.

[12] Also there is no necessity for gearing.

[13] In his latest models the writer uses strands even three times and not twice as long, viz. fourteen strands 43 in. long.

[14] This refers to $1/_{16}$ in. square sectioned rubber.

[15] Of uniform breadth and thickness.

[16] In practice I find not quite so high a proportion as this is always necessary.

[17] Steel pinion wire is very suitable.

[18] See Appendix.

[19] As high a pressure as 250 atmospheres has been used.

[20] There was a special pump keeping the water circulating rapidly through the boiler, the intense heat converting some of it into steam as it flowed. The making of this boiler alone consumed months of work; the entire machine taking a year to construct, with the best mechanical help available.

[21] Model Steam Turbines. "Model Engineer" Series, No. 13, price 6*d.*

[22] See Introduction, note to § 1.

[23] The voltage, etc., is not stated.

[24] *Note.*—Since the above was written some really remarkable flights have been obtained with a 1 oz. model having two screws, one in front and the other behind. Equally good flights have also been obtained with the two propellers behind, one revolving in the immediate rear of the other. Flying, of course, with the wind, *weight* is of paramount importance in these little models, and in both these cases the "single stick" can be made use of. *See also* ch. iv., § 28.

[25] *See also* ch. viii., § 5.

[26] Save in case of some models with fabric-covered propellers. Some dirigibles are now being fitted with four-bladed wooden screws.

[27] Vide Appendix.

[28] Vide Equivalent Inclinations—Table of.

[29] One in 3 or $0 \cdot 333$ is the *sine* of the angle; similarly if the angle were $30°$ the sine would be $0 \cdot 5$ or $\frac{1}{2}$, and the theoretical distance travelled one-half.

[30] *Flat-Faced Blades.*—If the blade be not hollow-faced—and we consider the screw as an inclined plane and apply the Duchemin formula to it—the velocity remaining the same, the angle of maximum thrust is $35\frac{1}{4}°$. Experiments made with such screws confirm this.

[31] Cavitation is when the high speed of the screw causes it to carry round a certain amount of the medium with it, so that the blades strike no undisturbed, or "solid," air at all, with a proportionate decrease in thrust.

[32] In the Wright machine r.p.m. = 450; in Blériot XI. r.p.m. = 1350.

[33] Such propellers, however, require a considerable amount of rubber.

[34] But *see also* § 22.

[35] "Flight," March 10, 1910. (Illustration reproduced by permission.)

[36] According to the author's views on the subject.

[37] Nevertheless some models with a very low aspect ratio make good flyers, owing to their extreme lightness.

[38] The chief advantage of cane—its want of stiffness, or facility in bending—is for some parts of the machine its chief disadvantage, where stiffness with resilience is most required.

[39] This is a good plan—not a rule. Good flying models can, of course, be made in which this does not hold.

[40] This is in theory only: in practice the monoplane holds both records.

[41] The best position for the propellers appears to be one in front and one behind, when extreme lightness is the chief thing desired.

[42] Because the number of strands of rubber in each bunch will be much less.

[43] Mr. Burge Webb claims a record of 500 yards for one of his.

[44] Flying, of course, with the wind.

Note.—In the "Model Engineer" of July 7, 1910, will be found an interesting account (with illustrations) of Mr. W.G. Aston's 1 oz. model, which has remained in the air for over a minute.

[45] These remarks apply to rubber driven motors. In the case of two-power driven propellers in which the power was automatically adjusted, say, by a gyroscope as in the case of a torpedo—and the *speed* of each propeller varied accordingly—the machine could, of course, be easily steered by such means; but the model to carry such power and appliances would certainly weigh from 40 lb. to 60 lb.

[46] Another and better way—supposing the model constructed with a central rod, or some suitable holdfast (this should be situated at the centre of gravity of the machine) by which it can be held in one hand—is to hold the machine with both hands above the head, the right hand grasping it ready to launch it, and the left holding the two propellers. Release the propellers and allow them a brief interval (about half a second) to start. Then launch boldly into the air. The writer has easily launched 1½ lb. models by this means, even in a high wind. Never launch a model by one hand only.

[47] Report on First Exhibition of Aeronautical Society of Great Britain, held at Crystal Palace, June 1868.

[48] The better way, undoubtedly, is to allow the competitor to choose his direction, the starting "circle" only to be fixed.

[49] Or 10 per cent. for duration of flight.

[50] In another competition, held under the rules and regulations of the Kite and Model Aeroplane Association for the best all-round model, open to the world, for machines not under 2 sq. ft. of surface, the tests (50 marks for each) were:—A. Longest flight in a straight line. B. Circular flight to the right. C. Circular flight to the left. D. Stability and landing after a flight. E. Excellence in building of the model.

[51] On the assumption that the model will fly straight.

[52] If permitted to enter; if not see Fig. 53.

[53] The design is patented.

Booksophile
Your Local Online Bookstore

Buy Books Online from
www.Booksophile.com

Explore our collection of books written in various languages and uncommon topics from different parts of the world, including history, art and culture, poems, autobiography and bibliographies, cooking, action & adventure, world war, fiction, science, and law.

Add to your bookshelf or gift to another lover of books - first editions of some of the most celebrated books ever published. From classic literature to bestsellers, you will find many first editions that were presumed to be out-of-print.

Free shipping globally for orders worth US$ 100.00.

Use code "Shop_10" to avail additional 10% on first order.

Visit today
www.booksophile.com